Starving Souls

A Spiritual Guide
to Understanding Eating Disorders

Anorexia, Bulimia, Binging...

Starving Souls

A Spiritual Guide
to Understanding Eating Disorders

Anorexia, Bulimia, Binging...

Rabbi Dovid Goldwasser

KTAV Publishing House, Inc.
Jersey City, NJ

Library of Congress Cataloging-in-Publication Data

Goldwasser, Dovid.
  Starving souls : a spiritual guide to understanding eating disorders : anorexia, bulimia, binging / Dovid Goldwasser.
    p. cm.
  Includes index.
  ISBN 978-1-60280-142-4
  1. Eating disorders--Religious aspects--Judaism. 2. Health--Religious aspects--Judaism. 3. Physical fitness--Religious aspects--Judaism. 4. Self-care, Health. I. Title.
  BM538.E38G65 2010
  296.7--dc22
                          2010001241

Published by
KTAV Publishing House, Inc.
930 Newark Avenue, Jersey City, N.J. 07306
www.ktav.com
Email: orders@ktav.com
Phone: 201-963-9524 • Fax: 201-963-0102

CONTENTS

CONTENTS

ברכת צדיק

דורינו - דור יתום - זכינו לאור גדול, מגדלור, שמפיץ אור לכל בני הגולה.

בעת גמר הספר פניתי אל הרב הגאון הגדול רבי חיים קנייבסקי שליט"א, והרצתי לפניו בכתב על כמה שאלות בנוגע למחלות אנורקסיה ובולימיה וכו', וזכיתי שבגלל נחיצות הדבר התייחס אל הנושא בחשיבות רב, ותיכף השיב עליהם:

האם מותר להסתיר מחלה זו בשביל שידוך המדובר?

בטח שאסור! שהרי היא מחלה, מחלה שהיא חולי נפש צריכים למסור.

כיון ששכיח בין החולים שמיד אחרי האכילה מתכוונים להקיא המאכלים כדי שלא ישארו במעייהם, האם מחויבים הם לברך ברכת המזון?

שאלה זו שאלתי פעם החזון איש ואמר כיון שאכלו ובאו לידי שביעה כבר נתחייבו בברכת המזון, וזה שהשקיאו המאכלים לא נפטרו בכך מידי חיובם ברכת המזון.

האם נכון לעשות מי שבירך לחולי נפש אלו?

אודאי, צריכים להתפלל עליהם, שהרי חולים הם, והיא חולי נפש.

וסיים ברכתו הק': **ברכה והצלחה על הספר.**

IRA M. SACKER, M.D.
19 West 34th Street, PH Floor
New York, NY 10001
212-268-4440

September 3, 2009

Rabbi Dovid Goldwasser is my respected colleague and friend for over twenty-five years. He is truly a "spiritual pioneer" in helping individuals and families deal with secrecy and the devastating effects of eating disorders in the community. It is my pleasure to support this new book by Rabbi Goldwasser that offers hope, insight, and inspiration to those and their families who have been touched by an eating disorder.

I have been in the medical profession as an Eating Disorders Specialist for forty years. Through many of those years I have been a witness to the "spiritual therapy" of Rabbi Goldwasser. He brings healing to the ones struggling with an eating disorder and he illuminates the darkness by educating the families that are deeply impacted.

Ira M. Sacker, M.D.,
*Author of Regaining Your Self
and Dying to Be Thin*

RUSSELL MARX, M.D.
The University Medical Center at Princeton

Starving Souls is a brilliant synthesis of the deepest levels of Jewish thought and a modern understanding of the causes and treatment of eating disorders. Scholarly, practical and wise it will be helpful to all who suffer from an eating disorder, love someone with an eating disorder or treat someone with an eating disorder. As Rabbi Nachman of Bratslav said, "There are those who eat in order to study and there are those who study to know how to eat."

Starving Souls is the best book available in this area to help sufferers achieve recovery.

Russell Marx, MD
Medical Director
Eating Disorders Program
The University Medical Center at Princeton

Treasurer and Member, Board of Directors
National Eating Disorders Association

SCOTT M. KESSLER, M.D.
MOUNT SINAI HOSPITAL, NEW YORK CITY

As a physician and friend of Rabbi Goldwasser, I have witnessed personally his phenomenal capacity to heal the body and the mind through his inspirational manner of communication and his extraordinary warmth and caring. His insight into the complexities of emotional stress and the physical manifestations of such stress on the body is nothing less than miraculous. I am in awe of his talents, his knowledge, and his ability to touch one's soul so directly and so deeply.

Scott M. Kessler, MD
Attending Physician/
Clinical Assistant of Otolaryngology
Mount Sinai Hospital, New York City

MARTIN FISHER, M.D.
CHIEF, DIVISION OF ADOLESCENT MEDICINE
MEDICAL DIRECTOR, EATING DISORDERS PROGRAM
Schneider Children's Hospital
North Shore – Long Island Jewish Health System

PROFESSOR OF PEDIATRICS
New York University School of Medicine

In the 1970's and 1980's, when the Division of Adolescent Medicine of Schneider Children's Hospital developed an eating disorders program at the Long Island Jewish Medical Center, and began seeing girls (and some boys) with anorexia nervosa and bulimia, only a few of those patients came from the observant community. Thirty years later we treat over 300 new children and adolescents with eating disorders each year, many of whom are observant. It is not clear whether the large number of eating disorders cases in the observant community is due to the growth of their population generally, to an increased risk of eating disorders in their families, or to improved awareness in the community. What is clear is that it has become crucial that all members of the community, including parents and teens and teachers and rabbis, familiarize themselves with eating disorders and how they are detected and treated.

One individual who has taken this responsibility very seriously is Rabbi Dovid Goldwasser. For many years now, Rabbi Goldwasser has worked tirelessly both to educate the community on understanding and responding to eating disorders and to guide individuals and families in seeking and receiving necessary and appropriate treatment. And of special importance, while our program and others that treat eating disorders focus on the medical, nutritional and psychological aspects, Rabbi Goldwasser adds the spiritual dimension. In the "multidisciplinary" approach currently used for the treatment of eating disorders, rabbinic input and a spiritual component have become increasingly important for many of the observant youth and their families that we work with.

I am therefore delighted that Rabbi Goldwasser has drawn on his considerable experience to offer up knowledge and chachma in a book that will now be available to the community and to those families and individuals experiencing eating disorders. I wish him continued hatzlachah in the important work that he is doing.

Martin Fisher, M.D.

ACKNOWLEDGMENTS

The Vilna Gaon remarked that at each juncture of accomplishment in our life, we have to remember to thank Hashem for the Divine assistance we were granted. I humbly thank Hashem for giving me the privilege to be involved in many different endeavors on behalf of the *klal.* It is through some of this work that I have had the opportunity to meet precious *nefashos,* some of whose stories grace the pages of this book. May Hashem grant me the wisdom and insight to continue helping His children and to bring glory to His Name.

To Martin E. Friedlander, Esq., a unique leader whose concern for the *klal* is unending. His *mesiras nefesh* and keen interest in every aspect of this *sefer* is responsible for its publication.

To Elliot Iglicki, an outstanding *askan,* who quietly and unassumingly works with great love for the *klal.* His enthusiasm and zeal for *mitzvos* is infectious; his commitment to his brethren is inspiring.

To Paul and Elisheva Stadler for their special *kesher* and their love for Torah that knows no bounds. Paul and Elisheva are a special couple whose dedication to *chinuch* has been a personal source of inspiration.

To Zelig and Sarah Bergman, pillars of our community and paragons of true service to Hashem for all to emulate. Blessed with a Torah perspective, their partnership in all that I am involved in has been invaluable.

To Avigdor Elimelech and Gitty Salgo, whose involvement in many different endeavors on behalf of the *klal* has made a great difference to many people. In a modest and humble way they carry on the golden *mesorah* of Torah and *chesed.*

To Amber Gristak for her contribution in editing this book. We feel privileged that she has lent her considerable talents to this project.

A special tribute to R' Moshe Mansour for his constant support and encouragement.

To Shlomo and Naomi Mayer, patrons of Torah, whose understanding of and sensitivity to the needs of the *klal* have made the world a better place. I thank them for their encouragement and *chizuk* over the years.

To Barry and Elinor Siegel, and Rebecca Siegel, whose involvement with the *klal* has enhanced our community.

My heartfelt appreciation to my colleagues and friends in the medical community, whose understanding of and sensitivities to the observant population is heartening. Their cooperation and collaboration in facilitating treatment have been gratifying.

The pen is too feeble an instrument to adequately thank Mrs. Simi Eichorn for all her work. The Almighty has blessed her with unusual *kochos,* and I thank her for sharing them with the *klal.* The numerous projects that I have been involved in over the years all bear her imprimatur.

To Bernard Scharfstein and Adam Bengal of KTAV Publishing whose sterling reputation is well-deserved. Their ground-breaking efforts in the field of publishing have raised the bar for literary classics. The vast contributions of KTAV have inspired people the world over.

To Diana Drew for her masterful job as copy editor; to Devorah Shadimoasser for her technical assistance; and to Hillel Engel, professional photographer, for his services.

ACKNOWLEDGMENTS

To R' Avrohom Kay, a master artist, for creating the striking cover and lending his expertise to this project. Over the past two decades it has been a *zechus* for me to work together with him on so many different endeavors.

To R' Eliezer and Gitty Allman; Eddie and Helene Appelbaum; Mr. and Mrs. Yoram Ben-Yishai; Rabbi Yochanan Donn; Rabbi Yosef Gesser; Rabbi Shmuel Grossman; Rabbi Moshe Kolodny; Jonathan and Yehudis Lewis; R' Duvy and Feige Neuhauser; Sonja Samokovlija; Dassy Siff; and Howie and Rochelle Sirota for their support and assistance.

With special appreciation to Rabbi Eliezer Ozer, Rosh Yeshiva of Yeshivat Lomza of Petach Tikvah.

A special note of thanks to Rabbi Chesky and Fayge Holtzberg and Rabbi Bentzion and Dassy Schechter.

To Sheya Mendlowitz, whose raison d'etre is to bring joy to *Klal Yisroel*. His magnificent contributions to the Jewish community worldwide attest to his manifold talents.

With special thanks to Mr. Jerry Greenwald, Mrs. Naomi Mauer, and Mr. Steve Walz of the Jewish Press.

To Nachum Segal, renowned radio personality, a master of words, and an eloquent spokesman for *Klal Yisroel*. It has been a privilege to work together with R' Nachum for more than two decades. His unique talents and efforts have united people from all walks of life.

Forever etched in my *neshamah* is the selfless dedication of my beloved parents, R' Yitzchak ben R' Yeruchem and Riva Tzirna bas R' Benzion z"l. May the example of their noble lives always serve as a source of inspiration and blessing.

My esteemed father-in-law, R' Chaim Baruch ben HaRav Elimelech z"l, whose life was dedicated to Torah and *chesed*, and continues to serve as an inspiration for our entire family.

To the honored matriarch of our family, Mrs. Esther Koval, who carries on the royal lineage of the distinguished Kovalenko and Fink families.

To my *eishes chayil,* Hinda Chaya, whose wisdom, insight, fortitude and understanding are a wellspring of *chizuk* for our entire *mishpacha.* Her enthusiasm and dedication are the foundation of my work on behalf of the *klal.*

May we merit much *nachas* from our children and our grandchildren as they follow in the footsteps of their great ancestors.

Rabbi Dovid Goldwasser
Chanukah, 5770

Introduction

Man has been veritably placed in the midst of a raging battle. For all of the affairs of the world, whether for the good or for the bad, are trials to a man: Poverty on the one hand and wealth on the other, serenity on the one hand and suffering on the other, so that the battle rages from both sides. If he is victorious on all sides, he will be the "Whole Man".

R' Moshe Chaim Luzzato, Path of the Just

One may ask: Why, indeed, are we subjected to these never-ending tests? And perhaps more important: how can we emerge victorious in this lifelong battle?

Such is life. Indeed, we pray every morning that we not be subjected to *nisyonos* (challenges). Rabbi Eliyahu Dessler explains that we are asking only that we not be tested severely; we ask that we be presented only with *nisyonos* that are not difficult to overcome. And we ask that we be granted the strength to overcome even the smaller ones. The truth is that the *nisyonos* that are sent our way are for our benefit. They are part of the Divine plan to spur us on to greater faith, and to develop greater depth of character and soul.

Man is presented with two types of challenges in life: Some challenges we can understand; they involve daily dilemmas in life relating to relationships with our fellow man or questions of propriety. Other tests, though, are more trying, with no reasonable explanation. These cause profound pain and terrible suffering.

The challenge of an eating disorder is one of the most mysterious and unfathomable, and its sheer force makes it seem hopeless.

It was a late Monday night, long after Maariv, and the phone rang. On the other end of the line were two frantic parents calling from Mexico City. Their son had just been discharged from an eating disorders program, but he had a very long road ahead of him for any hope of recovery. The parents were distraught and overwhelmed. They were desperately seeking guidance and assistance, and they wanted me to personally meet with their son as well.

As I listened to their brief account, I realized that the young man was not physically able to travel in his condition. There was silence at the other end, until the mother – with great hesitation in her voice – softly said, "Please don't take affront, but is there any possibility at all that we could arrange for you to come here?"

I could not close my eyes and ears to their despair and tears. I agreed to be there early Wednesday morning and canceled all my commitments for that day.

At the airport, the father came rushing over to greet me. He couldn't say a word; he just kept embracing me. When he could finally speak, he asked in a choked voice, "Do you think there is any hope? Will our son survive?"

On the drive to their home, Meir's father filled me in on the details. Coming from an upper-middle-class home, Meir had been a promising scholar at the top of his class throughout high school, until his senior year. Then there was a drastic change. He began to rapidly lose weight and distanced himself from family and friends. His affect was depressed. He lost all interest in his studies and there was a severe drop in his grades.

They immediately consulted all the medical professionals, but they were unable to effect any significant improvement. After a few months, Meir's health deteriorated to the point where he had to be rushed to the hospital and was then admitted into an inpatient eating disorders program for treatment. This was the first day home for Meir since then.

At the house, I was ushered into the study, where I met Meir. Slightly built, but noticeably emaciated, he nevertheless had a sharp mind and was very bright. He talked about his life, his dreams, his trials and tribulations. We discussed what was happening to him. Meir also asked me some halachic questions about eating disorders, which he felt needed a personal answer from me.

I was deeply moved after talking to Meir for a couple of hours. At one point he had taken out a photo album with pictures of himself. I could see that there was only a faint resemblance today to the healthy Meir before the ED.

Then Meir broke down and began to cry bitterly. He confided that he had begun to feel worthless, compared to others. He had become anxious about graduating and leaving the safe and nurturing environment for the outside world. He was afraid of failure. His self-esteem had plummeted and he didn't know where to turn.

"Rabbi," he moaned, "I don't know how I got like this! I must really be crazy."

I spent the entire day in that room with Meir talking about various topics. We barely scratched the surface of the deep-seated issues that were wreaking havoc on Meir's life.

At 5:00 P.M., Meir's father knocked on the door. According to the protocol of Meir's therapy, it was time for him to eat. His food had been prepared, exactly according to the meal plan, in the dining room. I remained in the study in order to give Meir his privacy as he ate.

Meir's father came rushing back. "Please, Rabbi Goldwasser," he said, "Meir asked if you would mind joining him as he eats."

"Are you sure this was Meir's idea?" I asked.

"Most certainly," he assured me.

I sat down across from Meir and watched as Meir broke off a minute piece of a saltine cracker. It was no bigger than what a bird could peck at with its beak. Meir held the crumb between his fingers a few inches from his mouth. One could actually see his mind struggling with the thought that he would have to put this in his mouth. As he studied the cracker crumb, his grimace and furrowed brow reflected the inner turmoil and conflict that he was experiencing.

I was totally caught unawares, though, when I noticed a large bead of sweat roll down his forehead, as Meir slowly edged the tiny piece of cracker into his mouth. Meir's laborious effort was a sight I will never forget.

I immediately thought of the *pasuk* in *Bereishis (3:19)*, *"Bezei'as apecha tochal lechem* – by the sweat of your brow shall you eat bread." It is an understanding that is uniquely applicable to those afflicted by eating disorders. Meir's personal struggle is symbolic of the hundreds of thousands of individuals who grapple with this experience every day of their lives.

Over the past eighteen years, there has unfortunately, been a dramatic increase in the manifestation of eating-disordered patients. At the outset, I would receive a call or letter once or twice a month. Today, I receive at least one or two calls or letters every day. From around the world, I listen to parents in crisis and read tearful correspondence from desperate individuals begging for answers, suggestions, recommendations for treatment, and some words of *chizuk*.

I have met people from all backgrounds and every point on the spectrum who are affected with anorexia, binge disorder, bulimia, or the like. The illness cuts across all socioeconomic and religious groups. It affects the young, even at elementary-school age, and strikes the old, including aging senior citizens. The illness knows no bounds. It is all-encompassing – physical, mental, and spiritual — and its insidious nature poses immense challenges for patients who are trying to reclaim their good health and mental equilibrium. The body may feel the pain, but it is the soul that is hurting.

We learn in *Pirkei Avos (Ethics of our Fathers, 5:26)*, "Turn it over and go through it, for everything is in it" – the answers to all of life's challenges can be found in the Torah. To be sure, it is of utmost importance that a person seek out the proper professional guidance – medical and otherwise – to deal with this malady.

With the help of Hashem, I have been privileged to make inroads, together with my distinguished colleagues in the medical profession, among those who are suffering from eating disorders. While the success stories are gratifying, I have witnessed the ignorance and lack of information that still exists concerning eating disorders. I have seen and heard people place inappropriate emphasis on diet and body image.

Finally, I have witnessed too many precious souls slipping in the battle to keep their souls alive.

I pray to Hashem that this humble offering will guide people, ease their pain as they recognize that others share their burden, and inspire a deeper understanding and insight into the extent of suffering and misery that exists in the complex world of eating disorders.

I dedicate this book in tribute to the starving souls throughout the world who struggle to live a normal life. May Hashem help them to emerge from the battle victorious, to once again become whole and fulfilled individuals.

LISA'S STORY:

A VOICE BEHIND THE DISORDER

The following pages are a record of actual correspondence that took place between the author and a 22-year-old young lady suffering from an eating disorder. Names and uniquely distinctive information have been changed in order to protect the identity of the patient.

You will read of the struggle and pain, the ups and the downs, the internal battles and a search for peace that is typical for most patients with eating disorders. These letters are enlightening, but they will sometimes shock and horrify the reader due to the extreme nature of the illness at various stages. As you read through the letters, you will gain genuine insight into the thought processes, the psyche, and the mind-set of an individual in the throes of an ED. I have spent numerous hours counseling Lisa. She is a highly intelligent young lady who is blessed with many talents. She is bright, inherently upbeat, and has a joie de vivre that will ultimately be indomitable.

Eating disorders cannot be blamed on the victims, nor can they be held accountable for becoming statistics. ED is a complex disease that stems from a confluence of interpersonal family and social dynamics and involves established psychological, emotional and behavioral factors.

As we communicated, I noted at one point that the Hebrew word for letter is *michtav (mem, chaf, taf, vais)*, whose numerical value *(gematria)* is 462. This corresponds to the Hebrew words *"lech echol b'simcha... – go and eat your bread with happiness... " (Koheles 9:7).* May we indeed merit to see the day when eating disorders are eradicated from society.

Lisa has asked me to share her thoughts and feelings so that the anguish and distress that she has endured will not be in vain. Her heartfelt wish is to be able to help others suffering from eating disorders. Lisa is hopeful that her personal account will validate their feelings, corroborate what they are going through, and facilitate their recovery. As she writes, "I wish I could give a present to everyone who is suffering: a day living like a normal person…"

Dear Rabbi Goldwasser,

Thank you so much for taking me seriously. Others I called for help and advice did not listen to me and told me that I'm fine, and I probably have a complex and I'm just overeating a little.

I feel a lot better because of all the support and help you've given me so far. And I feel more optimistic and hopeful about myself, my future and life in general.

Here's what I ate so far today:

8:15 A.M.   *Orange*

9:30 A.M.   *Sandwich – was really hungry on the way to work. Should not have eaten all of it; I was totally full after eating half. I made a mistake. Feel a little bloated.*

11:30 A.M.   *Extra-large salad. Not hungry. Don't know why I ate it. I think I was bored; I was waiting to call you.*

2:30 P.M.   *Extra-large chocolate bar, the big family one. Fruit roll-up and two big cups of chocolate milk. I feel yuk bloated and let down by myself and my behavior. Feel bad. I wasted my parents' money AGAIN … I think I ate this because on the way home from work I stopped in the store. I saw a girl in* my class with her husband and baby. Honestly, I'm not jealous of her; I'm very happy for her, for what she is blessed with. But it hurts me no end to see someone in my class like that when I am not blessed in that way yet. Maybe also because my iPod wasn't working. I listen to my iPod literally hours a day. I think this is because I can't bear hearing the voice inside me. It's not exactly sweet and encouraging at this state, so I block it out with music.

5:15 P.M.   I feel disgusting. Forced myself to drink three cups of water to wash everything down. Changed, because didn't fit into the clothes I put on this morning.

6:00 P.M.   Attacked the ice cream container, rice kugel, mandarin oranges, French toast, big bowl of soup, can't remember what else ... Feel yuk; face is blown up.

7:45 P.M.   Cookies, wafers, ice cream sandwich, ice cream. I don't even think I tasted these things, they were just stuffed down my throat ...

10:45 P.M.   Couscous, apple

Thank you again for everything – Lisa

 **WEDNESDAY**

Dear Lisa:

I just received your e-mail and have gone over it a couple of times. You have it set up very clearly. I want to wait until I see two or three days more before I comment.

I am also happy that you feel a bit more optimistic and hopeful. You have great potential, and *b'ezras Hashem,* I am confident that you will have a lot of *hatzlacha* in the future.

LISA'S STORY

**FRIDAY**

Thursday was okay till I got home at about 8 P.M. Got really out of control; was tired after a long day.

Now it's Friday morning, I feel yuk and out of control. Wish this would end. I'm very nervous because tomorrow the girls are getting together to celebrate my friend's upcoming wedding, and I have no choice but to go, and I won't fit in anything if I keep these disgusting eating habits up for the next day and a half. I'm not even thinking about the wedding on Wednesday night but at least it's on Wednesday so it leaves me four days to be normal.

Anyway this girl is two grades below me; she's really lucky to get married.

It's already 8:30 and I've eaten like crazy —bad bad start. Feel SICK.

I'm upset at myself because I ate milk —- cheesecake — before waiting after meat this week.* This is really rare – I think the second or third time in my life if I remember correctly. I'm scared.

Is this enough?

Thank you and good Shabbos.

Regards — Lisa

---

* According to Jewish law, one must wait a designated amount of time after eating meat before partaking of dairy foods.

Started off the day not too well, but not terrible, so I can't complain. Ate pretty big, high calorie breakfast then felt yuk and didn't want to totally lose it before the afternoon party, so I went for walk.

By lunch was not hungry. All I had was challah and one spoon of meat. Then, like two hours after lunch I actually felt hungry. Real miracle. Felt great to have that feeling. I ate some salad.
Then at the party I only ate some challah.
Saturday night I had challah and some egg salad.

Then I had like three pieces of cheesecake a few hours later- felt terrible and upset that I let go, but I knew that I wanted the cake and I was able to stop after I satisfied that craving, I didn't go to the freezer or bakery afterwards and stuff myself — maybe because I knew I have a wedding coming up (?).

LISA'S STORY

Dear Lisa:

I received yesterday's e-mail. Needless to say, I am concerned. I want things to start to pick up for you, to go better. It is certainly understandable that the challenges are great, especially around the time of a friend's wedding. These are the times when we need to exercise the greatest caution, in order not to have a setback. I wish that I could talk with you in person and try to better help you see your way out of this.

Believe me, anything that I can possibly do for you from here, long distance, I am certainly ready to do it. I had an idea that just might work for you. It is a reward system that considers the number of days that have passed without an episode as a "positive unit."

You take a calendar and for each day that you're able to have good feelings – and you did not either binge or purge – you make a special notation on that date. You continue each day and hopefully will be able to build up a positive unit of a number of days. In this way, you chart your progress and see that you're actually "successful" a number of days, which may well be the impetus to go a little further and strive for more. At the end of a certain period of time – days or weeks – we give ourselves a reward for having reached that milestone. The reward can be things that you like – going somewhere, or buying something special – so that there is a positive experience associated with the times that we are able to stick to our goal. It may work for you.

Please continue to let me know each day how you're doing. I know that you're trying, and you get great credit for that alone.

Looking forward to hearing from you. Good luck!

Woke up feeling amazing. Not dizzy or sick or bloated. But of course stuffed myself up and I'm all bloated, disgusting and feel like I let myself down once again.

Now back to step one: I have to start fighting myself again. Hope I lose all the weight I put on today; otherwise I probably just won't show up at the wedding.

I think why this happened today is because I'm really bored (not working today or tomorrow). I took my siblings to the park this morning and in the afternoon was totally bored so I went to bed. But I hate going to bed in the middle of the day and wasting time. Then I finally got up and that's when I totally lost it.

I feel numb.

Woke up this morning not feeling well after yesterday but once again covered up as if everything's OK.

I was upset at myself for ruining my opportunity to go to the wedding and feel good because it will take a good few days to get back to what I was yesterday before I messed up. So of course I ate today like crazy. Feel really yuk. Now my face is all blown up and I feel very uncomfortable.

Guess I'll try again tomorrow.

Thanks a lot!

Dear Rabbi Goldwasser,

Hi, how are you? Sorry about Thursday night. Really felt horrible and wanted to run away but you can run away from everyone but yourself. I'm just really angry at myself and Hashem.

So practically what can I do?

Rabbi Goldwasser suggested looking at the word emunah [faith] which I don't know how to get hold of. The other idea that sounded really amazing and helpful was the one with the sponsor and again I have no idea where to find one. The only thing I thought of today was maybe to look for someone here online but I'm not sure if that will work so well.

I was thinking are there any really good, helpful and practical books that I can read? Or Internet sites? I obviously read a huge amount to pull through till now - I think I read every book in the library under this topic, but there must be more.

Thank you again for everything,

Half bowl of cereal
5 mini ice creams
Egg sandwich
2 mini ice creams
1 XXL ice cream
Chocolate mousse cake
3 large hot dogs
Sweet potato
Pumpkin
2 Laffy Taffys
A little bit of meat
Hot dog in a roll
Apple

Probably more, but I can't remember. So I felt a little dizzy and weak about 7 o'clock so I ate meat. I thought it would make me feel better and counteract all the sugar from yesterday and today.

Not sure why this all happened. Had a really terrible day. I feel like I took a few steps forward and now I'm falling like 10 steps back.

Here's a few ideas what I think might be behind all of this:

My sister went out yesterday with her 10th or 11th boy – can't remember exactly. I feel she's lucky. Fine, she's not engaged, and this boy is not working out — but she's still going out and feels like things are moving.

My boss got really upset at me. Feel stupid and I don't feel it was totally my fault.

I am really bored with my life.

I don't feel like I need to look good for anything so I don't care enough to control myself, which would obviously make me look better.

Basically not looking forward to anything.

TUESDAY

Dear Lisa:

I read your latest e-mail with interest. Thank you for being so honest and open.

We must get you on a regular program of healthy eating. I will try to get you a few different programs that you can choose from.

You certainly took a few steps forward; when you go back you only take one step back.

Concerning your sister: do not look at the boys she goes out with. You have your own merits, and your sister has her own separate merits. Believe me when I tell you, Hashem has a special marriage partner in store for you. Things will move, and at the exact right time you will be the happiest bride in the world.

Concerning your boss: do not worry. The fact that he got upset at you — that's what bosses do. I am sure that you are a great employee and try your best every day. Just keep on and don't worry.

Concerning being bored with life: maybe we could get you some increased activities. Maybe you could do some volunteer work for a charity organization. I need to speak with you by phone to go over some ideas whenever you'd like.

Concerning not needing to look good: that whole psychology is something that you will need to rethink and work on. You don't need to look good for anybody except for yourself. Your positive self-image and self-esteem are more important, and will ultimately be the greatest source of happiness for you. Parenthetically, you can never tell when someone will notice you, on a day when you least expect it, and will think of suggesting a possible match for you.

 **TUESDAY**

Woke up not feeling well. I was all bloated— looked like I was having a baby. Felt yuk because I wasn't working, so I have to somehow live through the day and bend my back over, which is really uncomfortable because otherwise looks so weird and suspicious. Like yesterday I looked normal and today suddenly I look like I'm in my fourth or fifth month.

Chocolate mousse cake
2 bagels
Cake – a lot
2-3 bagels

That's so far today. It's 2 P.M. Feel like giving up. This seems too hard for me.

LISA'S STORY

Thank you.

My sickness made me forget that that I have to look good for myself. I really am trying to be better. Also today, thank God, I am feeling better. I don't know what happened yesterday.

By the way, I am actively trying to find another job; it's just hard here. Even now I work in public schools. I now have a 3-1/2 week vacation break so I'm not sure what to do. Anyway I hope things will smooth out. Whatever is happening now I can't understand and it seems very very difficult — for me at least — but I know for sure Hashem has a plan.

Thank you so much again for all your support and help.

⌇**THURSDAY**

Woke up feeling good (good for me but probably compared to a normal person just under good) because yesterday I didn't binge at night. I guess because I really wasn't feeling good by day and I was petrified.

Today I had an OK day (for my standards). I don't think I made the right food choices with everything I ate, and I definitely did overeat a little, but nothing compared to what I've done in the past. (Reading your e-mail helped me a lot, I feel, to achieve this.)

I lost some weight off my face so I feel more human. I really hope this keeps up.

Had a good start to the day, ate half a bowl of cereal.

Then a little later totally blew it with rich chocolate cream cake and chocolate milk. Dunno what will be. This is pure madness. I hope I won't totally lose it today. We're having guests tonight.

(The reason why I think I ate the above is because my brother is giving my parents some difficult days. My parents are very nervous and tense.)

That's so far for today; it's 9:30 A.M.

My mother took my brother to school and I'm home by myself. I'm so excited (even though the house is a mess and I have a long list of chores to complete). I never have some time like this that I can put on whatever CD I want and no one's home with me! I hope the cleaning lady comes late - she drives me nuts.

Thank-you. Good Shabbos!

∽SHABBOS

Recap what I wrote on Friday:
Breakfast:
Chocolate
Half bowl cereal
Shocolate cream cake

Lunch: fish

Before Shabbos:
3 Roma tomatoes,
A lot of rich chocolate cake -
Really upset I did this. I had a good day. My mother was so nice to me; after all I do love her surprisingly more than food, if that makes sense and I have a deep respect for her. I was hungry and wanted challah, but I knew if I ate it I wouldn't wash or bentsch [say the Grace After Meals], and I don't do that when I'm being good. I only do that when I'm having a really bad day. Anyway, you're not allowed to eat bread after midday on Friday, so cake was the only thing I found to eat. (This was like a few minutes before Shabbos because I got home very late.)

Friday night:
Was really full from the cake since I ate so much. So I had some challah and some soup and a bite of chicken - we had guests.

Honestly, comparing myself to myself, this was a pretty good day. I think! I know there is sooooo much room for improvement but I haven't had such a good bad day in a while!

Shabbos day

Breakfast
9:00 A.M.   _Half grapefruit and half banana; felt very full_

10:00 A.M.   _A lot of cream chocolate cake -ohhhh blew it! I know why I did this. I'll have to explain on the phone; it's too long to write_

11:00 A.M.   _More cake_

Lunch   _Really full — some challah, some salad and spoon of cholent, apple_

4:00 P.M.   _One regular ice cream cone. Really upset with myself. I know why I did this, but — again – complicated, weird reason. I'll have to explain on the phone._

5:00 P.M.   _Some challah — not hungry, but you're supposed to eat something, isn't that right? (I don't mean this is an excuse to eat. I really didn't want to eat, but something inside forces me to do it — maybe so Hashem doesn't punish me or so I can be forgiven for all the sins that I do with food.)_

6:10 P.M.   *2 more regular ice cream cones. Now this time I was really angry because I try not to eat before havdalah [marking the end of the Sabbath]. Now I really crossed the red line. (I know my red line is pretty far.) I dunno what to do with myself — maybe buy handcuffs. Just totally out of control. Hope Hashem forgives me and doesn't punish me.*

∽ SHABBOS NIGHT

Melava Malka

This is so funny really. I love my father; he makes me laugh so much. He bought me home some fresh yum challah for me for Melava Malka [special meal after the Sabbath].If only he knew ....maybe I should finally tell them. I dunno what to do, but if they get upset I'll have to leave home - but then I won't know where to go and I'll get very suicidal again. OK, forget it.

So Melava Malka I ate. I'll be honest, I wasn't hungry at all but I ate — I think — 7 pieces of challah if I remember correctly - unless I lost count because I ate so much, and some egg salad.

OK, I dunno whether to laugh or cry. Just read this over before sending it – I find this eating and changing clothes business really sad, and trust me it keeps me very busy all day.

I thought of an idea - do you have some names of people with eating disorders? I want to pray for them.

Thank you so much again – I'm sure I'm a really unique — meaning different, weird and uncommon probably interesting — case .

Have a good week.

Dear Lisa:

I hope this note finds you well. I received your past e-mails and read with interest, and certainly concern, what has been happening.

I just want you to know that I tried to reach you for two days and could not get through to your cell phone. Is it in operation? Either write or let me know how to contact you and go over what happened on Shabbos.

Please — whatever you do — do not negatively translate your father's or anyone else's actions. I am sure that everybody means very well. The problem is that we don't know sometimes that the things that we do upset others.

I will certainly give you the names of people with eating disorders you can pray for. The first one is Sarah, the daughter of Miriam. Send me as well your name and your mother's name so, if you would like, I could have others with ED pray for you.

In your letter you wrote again about the conflict between the eating disorder and Jewish law, particularly with the Havdalah service. You should know one thing. Hashem loves you, and Hashem understands you more than any other person in this world. Believe me, you will not be judged on eating or what you did because of the ED. You will only be given blessings and understanding. Forget about punishment. You only deserve reward for every day of struggle that you get through. I give you my word. Maybe some time we will have a chance to go into this further.

Please be in touch, and do not have any negative thoughts. Try to be your own best friend. With a humble prayer to Hashem that you have great blessing, success and healing,

Rabbi Dovid Goldwasser

LISA'S STORY

Thank you very much. I appreciate it, I really do.

My phone works. I don't know why the call didn't go through. I did get one missed call last night from a no caller- ID number, but aside from that I'm not sure what's wrong. But thank you and I will try to call when I have a chance.

I don't think I was clear about what happened with my father. I wasn't exaggerating. I really found it very funny. I really love when he buys me little things! It did make me happy.

Also regarding Jewish law: it's a real live scare that I have. I always feel very scared of Hashem. I feel so hopeless in almost every area of my life, for instance, I can't control the traffic or my livelihood. I can't control when I get married. (Yes, I can pray and then Hashem either says yes or no, but that's about it.) Aside from my reaction and attitude to situations, I can't control anything only Hashem can. Therefore I feel like this.

I don't know what is wrong with me and where I get such crazy ideas from. (Girls my age are not so nuts, as far as I know). Probably from my mother, because she is so strict and anything not permitted in halachah is inexcusable, e.g., wearing something that is not above and beyond modest (including all the extras). I don't think I'm making sense in what I wrote but that's how I feel.

Also, if I get rewarded for each day of struggle – that's only if I win the struggle. Because Hashem gave me this test and if I win I get rewarded, or let's just say a consequence of what you do (good or bad). I don't know anymore. I'm confused. And if Hashem loves me, why am I so messed up and why can't I get married?

21

All my progress with my ED is from Hashem; He helped me. I know that for sure because I alone can't fight myself. I'm too weak. I think most people are, if they want to be honest and admit that.

Now I totally contradicted myself but, honestly, this is how I feel.

Thanks again,
Regards

⟳ MONDAY NIGHT

Had an OK day.

My parents gave me a really beautiful birthday gift. I'm shocked and touched.

Can't remember exactly what I ate. I had a relatively good day, I think.

I wasn't feeling so good last night emotionally. Felt terrible and down went to bed as soon as I got home from work at 7:30.

⟳ TUESDAY

Today I feel good. I went for a walk with my mother in the morning.

8:00 A.M.   Half-bowl cereal

10:30 A.M.   Egg sandwich

I'll e-mail again later.

Thank you!!!

LISA'S STORY

 **TUESDAY**

Dear Lisa:

Hope this note finds you well.

Happy to hear that you got a job for the vacation; try not to work too hard! The *mishnah* in *Pirkei Avos* [Ethics of the Fathers] tells us that it's good to be busy.

I would like to address your thoughts on Jewish law and the Torah perspective. Permit me to express a few thoughts and feelings on your words.

Although I realize that you feel very frightened of Hashem, I hope to be able to show you a different way of understanding our relationship with Hashem.

The most important trait that we exercise in our relationship with Hashem is love. We must endeavor to feel the great love that Hashem has for us and respond in kind. We learn in the *Song of Songs*: "I alone am my Beloved's and my Beloved is mine" — that the greatest love that could ever exist is between us and Hashem. We also say in the special Shabbos *zemiros* [hymns] "My soul is lovesick for You," because we realize that the love of Hashem is a deep connection that the soul yearns for.

Also, of course, the Torah tells us to love Hashem.

My rebbi, the great Rabbi Avigdor Miller *ztl*, said that when you walk down the street, every once in a while, when nobody is looking, say "I love You, Hashem." Hashem celebrates our joyous occasions and cries for our pain. Hashem says – I will be with you at every sad time.

There are numerous verses in the Torah and the Talmud that help us to understand the proper Torah perspective on our relationship with Hashem. The Torah tells us to serve Hashem with fear, and our Sages explain that the fear we should feel is because we are afraid of losing that special, surreal bond of love that we have with Hashem.

Although you are correct that we do not have control over traffic, livelihood, marriage, etc. we are certainly far better off that Hashem conducts the world, for He ultimately knows what will be best for us and those things that we may even want very badly but are not good for us.

If we place our full *bitachon* [faith] in Hashem, and put our lives in His hands — as we say in our morning prayers, "I shall entrust my spirit into His hand" — then we will be confident and reassured that all will turn out well, especially those things over which we have no control. I don't think that you have crazy ideas at all, and I think that many people your age also have these ideas and questions.

There isn't any doubt that you are going to get married. There is no question that Hashem is saying yes to your prayers, and that you will meet a suitable young man. Don't falter in your faith even for a second.

Certainly, the topic of modesty lends itself to controversy. We need to understand what it means to "stay within the guidelines of modesty." Ultimately, the *Shulchan Aruch* [Code of Jewish Law] and rabbinic rulings must guide our lives. If you like, we can explore this in greater detail.

Please believe me that Hashem truly, truly loves you and I don't believe that you are messed up. You are right; Hashem has helped you with your ED and with life. You are never alone. Please remember the verse, "Hashem is with me and I will not fear."

Concerning contradictions: do not worry about them. It is very normal to have conflicting feelings, as *Mesilas Yeshorim* [Path of the Just] says, there is a war raging within us at different times of our lives. We work every day of our lives on our outlook and perspective *in* life. You are doing a great job. I will write you a separate e-mail concerning reward and struggles.

With best wishes for *bracha* [blessing] and *hatzlacha* [success].

 **TUESDAY**

Thank you for the letter. I read it carefully.

Regarding marriage, why can't I believe that everything will be OK and stop thinking that maybe this is my test? I can't stand myself.

Anyway, tons of speakers (at least the ones I listen to) don't speak or think this way and if they do they don't show it. They speak negatively and bring across the message of Hashem's din [judgment], strictness, and the strong idea of consequence and harsh punishment - things along these lines.

Thanks – Lisa

STARVING SOULS

(Recap of Tuesday)
8:00 A.M.	*Half bowl cereal*
10:30 A.M.	*Egg sandwich*
1:30 P.M.	*Banana*
3:00 P.M.	*Pepper*

Now I stuffed my day up

5:30 P.M.   2 pieces of chicken, a lot of stir fry - felt very full bloated and yuk
Ice cream cone, butternut

8:00 P.M.   Some vanilla pie slice

9:30 P.M.   2 apples
I know why this happened. I knew all the way. I don't know why I couldn't stop myself.

I left work at 5:00 P.M. and was really hungry. I ate lunch at 10:30 in the morning because I knew I wouldn't have a lunch break at work today. I worked from 11-5. Anyway, I knew dinner won't be ready and my siblings usually ask me to drive them somewhere, or help with their homework, or sit and listen to something that happened today. Anyway, I knew I should not have gone home. Instead I should have bought myself something to eat and just unwound in the car for 10 minutes before I went home. So I went to the bakery, but there was only unhealthy things and I was in a good mood and not craving anything, so I didn't want to buy anything. What I should have done was go somewhere else, but I didn't.

Anyway I went home. Of course, dinner wasn't ready so I warmed something up from last night because I didn't eat dinner last night — I just had a lot of cake and went to bed.

Anyway, I got upset and told my father that I knew I shouldn't have come home.

I could see he was hurt - he didn't say anything. He is really so so nice to me honestly. Then I got upset at myself and binged.

So today, hopefully, I will learn from my mistake and not go home straight away. Except, I don't know if it will apply today because I binged yesterday so I still feel so disgusting and full.

Dear Lisa:

Hope this note finds you well.

I wanted to express a few thoughts on the topic of Hashem's rewarding our struggles in life. As you remember, we started the discussion concerning the reward for one's struggle in this world.

It says in the Talmud, "We toil and they toil," meaning the peoples of the nations of the world. "We toil and receive reward; however, they toil and do not receive reward or payment."

The Chofetz Chaim asks: What does this mean? When we work we receive our salary, and when they work they receive their salary. He explains it so beautifully and elucidates the whole idea of reward in this world.

The Chofetz Chaim presents the example of a shoemaker who is given a pair of shoes to repair. If he fixes the pair of shoes, then he gets paid for the job. However, if he is unable to repair the shoes that someone brings him, he will not get paid, even if he spent a lot of time trying to repair the shoes.

With *Klal Yisroel* it's not the same. When we try to do *teshuvah*, when we try to *daven*, when we try to withstand various challenges in life — even if we were not successful but we tried, we put forth effort, we showed Hashem that we want to be good, we exerted ourselves, we toiled –- then Hashem gives us reward.

And that's why it says "we toil" – when we work, even if we didn't get to the finish line, we are rewarded. *Klal Yisroel* gets rewarded for the "work," meaning the effort, in contradistinction to the peoples of the nations of the world whose work, i.e., their "effort," is not calculated at all and there is no reward.

So you see, Lisa, it doesn't matter if you're able to win or finish or be completely successful. Hashem knows all that we go through. And when we struggle, and we show Hashem that we wish to get better, we wish to come closer, we are given credit for our effort and our struggles.

It is told that R' Chaim of Sanz was once together with his *chassidim* and they were deeply steeped in prayer. The aura was so emotional and inspirational that the entire assemblage was moved to tears. One of the *chassidim*, however, could not bring himself to tears, try as he would.

He quietly went into a small kitchen adjacent to the *bais medrash,* took an onion out of the pantry, which he cut in half, and then returned with it under his *tallis* to his place in the *bais medrash.* As he resumed his prayers, he surreptitiously brought the onion closer to his face and the tears began to stream from his eyes.

The Rebbe, however, saw what the *chassid* was doing, and when the *chassid* realized this he was overcome with embarrassment.

After the *davening,* when everyone else had left, the Sanzer quickly went over to the *chassid* and quietly remarked, "The Ribono Shel Oam was moved as much by your anguish over the fact that you weren't able to cry as He was by the actual tears of the other *chassidim.*"

B'ezras Hashem, we will continue on this topic.

With all good wishes for continued *hatzlacha* in all that you do.

8:00 A.M.   *2 hot bagels*
             Chocolate cream cake

10:30 A.M.   *Chocolate cream cake*

Don't know why I did this - stuffed my day up already - I think because I feel so yuk and full from last night and I feel so out of control and edgy, so I suppressed my feelings with food.

Oh! I feel fat — gained so much weight since last night!

Now it's about 2:30. I'm at work so I'll fill in the rest of the day later.

Thank you so much for all your help and support. It feels so good. For the past approximately six years I kept this all to myself.

Anyway, I want to just note that I have never really spoken to anyone with an eating disorder and obviously I never had anyone assess me. When I send you what I ate each day, I have no idea where you place me — meaning how deep or bad I am in this ED . But when I write what I eat lately I am pleasantly surprised. I haven't had trouble breathing in a while, thank God. And when I say I'm not feeling good, I don't feel well, but I can still get out of bed and don't feel as bad as I used to, and I don't binge as much as I used to.

An example of what I used to eat in a binge will be - (this is after I'm full) a few apples, a lot of cake, 5 bagels, extra-large chocolate bars and probably more – I just can't remember right now. So, thank God, my binges today are nothing like they used to be.

I was just thinking about this last night — even though I was bloated and bingeing and felt physically and emotionally yuk — but my older brother and

30

sister-in-law, who live in South Africa, are coming over next week. It's hard sometimes with a girl close to my age in the house. (My sister at home is a few years younger.) For example, she'll notice what I eat, etc. and just her personality - I love her and all, but honestly, it's not easy to deal with myself, my ED, and my sister-in-law.

Anyway, so I was just thinking how far I've come since I saw her last. I feel good about it for some weird reason, even though I still have a long way to go.

I don't know why I'm writing this but wasn't this supposed to be a diary where I can write whatever I want?

Anyway, this might sound weird but it is a reality for me. I live and breathe this — in the summer you can't wear a sweater because it looks funny when it's hot, and someone will probably tell you to take it off. Wearing a sweater/coat is the only way I cover myself up when I'm bloated. Now I just pretend that I'm cold even when I'm boiling . (I'm only my real size about once in 2-3 months for as long as it lasts, probably about 1-2 days — because most days I binge, unlike the books that I read that people binge two times a week, twice a month.)

Thank you so much again, and I hope to call soon. Lisa

Dear Lisa:

I hope this letter finds you well. Thank you for your letter and your thoughts.

I am very happy to hear that the current bingeing is nothing in comparison to your former bingeing. It is difficult for me to make an exact assessment from this far away, but I definitely feel that you are making strides.

You have at least recognized the "at risk" behaviors and very well understand at which points you feel a loss of control. It seems that the bingeing is triggered by various interactions, and a great deal of your feelings have to do with those you come in contact with most frequently.

You certainly have the strength and the power to overcome this ED. With the power of *tefillah* [prayer], positive thinking, and working through the issues you can certainly restore a norm of healthy and happy living for yourself.

Regarding your writing, you can certainly write whatever you want.

On the topic of wearing sweaters and coats even when it's warm: I must talk with you about it. It's all part of the cycle and reinforces the bingeing/upset/shame/cover-up etc. This too must be addressed.

Please feel free to call any time you find it necessary.

LISA'S STORY

(recap)

8:00 A.M.	*2 hot bagels*
	Chocolate cream cake
10:30 A.M.	*Chocolate cream cake*
3:00 P.M.	*2 apples*

Okay, so my everyday crazy routine — I come home from work and ruin everything.

6:00 P.M.	*Chocolate cream cake – fantastic! I finished the whole cake!*
	A lot of rice
	2-1/2 pieces of butternut
	A lot of salad

I think that was it. Don't remember. But I definitely do remember that I really wasn't hungry to begin with and I felt sick after.

I was out at night- met some shadchan (I'll explain on the phone) so I didn't eat all night. I only had some orange juice before bed; really wanted coffee but I was fleishig from the rice.

✑ THURSDAY MORNING

Thank you for the letter of Wednesday.

Regarding my crazy sweater business: I'm not sure if it's about covering up - maybe slightly - but honestly it's about one day looking okay and the next blown up and looking like I'm having a baby. I'm not joking. If I stand straight that's how I look — looks strange and probably arouses suspicion and looks weird!

I really wish I could get over this crazy thing. It's all in the mind - coming from myself, which is so ironic. Thanks again

I'll try to call today,
Lisa

I just reread the e-mail again. I just want to note I feel pretty much in line with my feelings in a certain way; i.e., I usually know my triggers. I agree 100% that most of my triggers are with my family. And that's probably because I barely get together with friends i.e., anyone else outside the family. But I don't understand why my seminary year was so messed up if I wasn't around family (I never told the rabbi what happened in sem, but I'll just say, in short, that it was an extremely bad year and — looking back — very taxing on my body - the ED part.)

It's just as we learned in school, "The distance between the brain and heart is probably the longest journey on earth."

Thanks again.
Lisa

LISA'S STORY

Dear Rabbi Goldwasser,

It's a funny thing! I always keep telling myself: Today's a new day and I have a new chance. But somehow today never comes. Maybe today will be the day....?

8:00 A.M.   Orange

10:00 A.M.   Hot bagel

12:00 P.M.   Apple and pear- feel yuk, bloated and full

My clothes are too tight now. Feel very down.

Thank you for the e-mail. I just tried to call a few times but no one answered.

I understand the message, although I don't understand clearly how it relates to me. Okay, I want to get better so badly but I don't always try – meaning, a lot of the time when I binge I sort of feel it's out of my control to stop and there is a monster coming out from inside of me that forces me to eat.

But technically it's my hands and mouth doing it, so I should have no excuse. So in this case I surely can't get rewarded?! I don't know; I'm confused.

Talking in the present, I have not eaten normally, i.e., not binged (if I remember correctly) in about two months. And even then I ate OK for — I think — 1 or 2 days tops.

Okay, I don't know why I'm writing this. It's got nothing to do with your e-mail. I'm just really fed up, sick of everything, feel a little suicidal. I'm not

35

at the stage that I'll actually do it, but I have those feelings.

And, yeah, I have nothing else to say. I just feel horrible.

Regards, Lisa

Dear Lisa:

I hope this note finds you well. I read your latest e-mail with interest. Of course, the major *nisayon* [challenge] for you is your routine when you come home.

Is it possible that you would accept a food plan, so that your eating would be regulated according to a balanced diet, allowing you to make choices in the various "food groups" while monitoring a schedule of meals and intake of food?

Please let me know if you're up for this, and I will try to provide some sample menus for you.

Please – this is very important – if you ever have suicidal thoughts, reach out to someone who could assist you immediately. Anyone locally – doctor, health care worker, relative, etc. This is extremely important. We need you here for 120 years. It is imperative to understand the great value and preciousness of your life.

I was sorry to hear that you're feeling very down. Rav Wolbe *ztl.* said there are days when everything is going up and we're feeling great, and days when everything is going down and we feel horrible. Vicissitudes of life happen to all of us – some of us have greater highs and some of us have greater lows; some of us have neither.

When you're experiencing a low, there are several things you can do to give yourself a boost. Of course, these are only things that can help while working through the underlying challenges.

1) Ask Hashem to help you, either through your own *tefillah* or you can have special *kavanah* [devotion] when you say the two *Yehi Ratzon* prayers [literally "May it be Your will, Hashem ...] that follow the morning *brachos* [morning prayer services] and the paragraph in the *Shemone Esrei*, "*Re'eh na b'anyeinu* – Behold our affliction". You could also say a chapter of *Tehillim* that you especially relate to, perhaps Chapters 21, 23, 121 or 130.

2) Do not dwell upon the past. The power of positive thinking and good thoughts cannot be underestimated. Try to "refrain," and think of things that make you happy. Think of an accomplishment or something you feel you did that had a positive effect on others. You can also think about future plans. Allow yourself to dream of a brighter future.

3) Read a *sefer* or a book that will give you inspiration. Listen to a *shiur* [lecture]. Contact a friend. Do an activity that you find enjoyable. Take up a hobby. Learn to play an instrument. Go outdoors, exercise, observe nature.

4) Write an e-mail and express yourself.

There are more ideas that can be helpful. Please let me know if you wish to discuss them.

I was very happy to hear that you met a *shadchan*. Even if you're not sure that anything will come from it, minimal *hishtadlus* [effort] is what is required. Reinforce positive thinking and have a lot of *bitachon*. I look forward to receiving an e-mail from you with good news.

With best wishes for *hatzlacha!*

(recap)

8 A.M.	*Orange*
10 A.M.	*Hot bagel*
12 P.M.	*Apple and pear*
3 P.M.	*Cherry tomatoes*

Not feeling good feel a little dizzy - still got two hours left at work - not sure why I feel like this maybe because I had a really bad night last night (after what the shadchan told me) and fell asleep late.

I'm all bloated and fat.

5 P.M.	*I binged and did a good job. I'm too embarrassed to write what I ate.*
8 P.M.	*Two bowls of soup, grapes, cabbage stir-fry* *I don't remember properly; I think that was it.*
8:30 P.M.	*Fruit roll-up*

Thoughts: I'm a professional binger. This is gehennom.

Usually I'm busy helping and go to sleep late Thursday night but, my father and mother went to visit a cousin in the hospital so after doing some jobs and errands I took a boiling bath - got a little burned. I read a book by someone who was first anorexic and then bulimic - sounds like me minus the exercise! I thought it was a fantastic book obviously because she went through it and her thoughts were so real and true. They were almost tangible for me and I

could relate so easily to her. I was a little jealous because she had such amaz-
ing family support.

I read another book written by two doctors. It was really a pathetic book be-
cause the doctors obviously only studied ED. There is no emotion or under-
standing or human element and they sounded like they believe that the
sufferers are in control and sort of just get up and get over it. Recovery is
***NOT** as simple as – okay, eat this, that and that and nothing else, and if you*
crave, e.g., peanut butter, then have one teaspoon and then everything will be
okay. They sounded like fools to me, so unrealistic in my opinion.

FRIDAY

Dear Rabbi Goldwasser,

Thank you for your e-mail.

Regarding the food plan: I guess I can give that a try. Why not? (Don't really
know how it will work because I can't make my mother cook what is on my
menu.) Even though I doubt that will work – It's sick. I am just totally
OUT OF CONTROL.

(Also, I really don't think this is a problem. Like when you sent me the
healthy eating article of course it's definitely good to read. But because I was
anorexic — by now I forgot how many calories things are — I know in my
sleep what's healthy and what's not and how to eat with balance. But, of
course, from knowing to doing........)

About calling someone – I have no one to call, honestly. I basically live my
life a secret. No one knows about the real me, i.e., my ED, besides Rabbi
Goldwasser. Were you able to find a sponsor for me?

I do try to dream and think of good things, but nothing has happened yet so I am discouraged.

About the shadchan, I wasn't clear. She was very insensitive and I was a little shocked that she said some things in front of me, e.g., boys want a lot of money and a lot of boys are not interested in girls from so far out of town. It will be hard, she said, because there are a lot of older singles and you can't be picky. You have to be willing to do / live wherever the boy wants, once the boy already agrees to meet you and things like that. Really, I don't feel like a person if this is the case. I can't have any wishes and an opinion. I just should go and do everything the boy wants, like I'm just an object. I definitely understand where she is coming from and there is truth in what she said, but I still felt like telling her that you're not supposed to tell that to a 22-year-old girl whose whole class is almost married and a lot of them did amazing shidduchim. I'm also sick and tired of these boys who will go out with me because something is funny about them e.g., father depressed, family not religious, a much older boy, etc. (Yes, I know I have a big problem — my ED — but no one knows this.)

Just rereading what I wrote. It's pretty funny. I'm a good complainer - but I just want you to know that now that I have someone to share my ED with everything is coming out. But this is so not me. I "wear" a thick mask each day- I seem so happy and easygoing to people.

A friend commented to me (don't remember the exact words but the message was) that I am such a happy single — not jealous of anyone in the class, just happy-to-be, but others in my class who are not married seem upset and nervous and want to get engaged already. She said she picked it up by some comments I make every so often. Funny - I thought just the opposite .

Thanks a lot,
Lisa

P.S. Although it is definitely correct that I usually binge after work, there are exceptions. Like you'll see on my food diary/e-mail, today is an exception because by 10 A.M. I totally lost it.

✐ FRIDAY AFTERNOON

Dear Lisa:

Hope this note finds you well.

Please never, never give up. A new food plan, positive thinking, the right moment, etc. may be just what is needed. Remember, as long as you still talk about it, and want to work things out, there is a lot of hope. I am currently looking for a sponsor for you — at least somebody who has been through an eating disorder — that you could speak with.

Concerning the *shadchan:* some people need to have a training course in sensitivity. There is no "rule" on *shidduchim.* The right person can come along and not *care* about any of the things that the *shadchan* mentioned. You have your own merits, and you have your own *mazal.* It is not dependent on any "statistics," any feeling about what's out there, or *shidduchim* from out-of-town. Also, please do not be discouraged that you might have been "*redd*" [suggested] less than desirable *shidduchim.* When the right one comes along, I pray that he will be your knight in shining armor.

Regarding wearing a mask: it's not such a bad thing. If people see you upbeat, *b'simcha* [happy], not jealous of anyone, it is only good for you and will impact in a most positive way. You know what they say: When you smile, the world smiles with you …

I was once together with the great Rosh Yeshiva, Rav Pam, and he mentioned that the face of a person is a *reshus harabbim* – it's a public domain – in contrast to the heart of the person which is a *reshus hayachid*, or a private domain. Therefore, when we interact with other people, we should wear a smile when we can, even if in our heart we may not be feeling so happy. Nevertheless, it is most important for us to be able to let out our feelings and thoughts in the proper venue at the right time.

In your writings, as sad as some are, there is an element of *simcha*. Hopefully, with time, the *simcha* will triumph.

Please let me know your feelings on this. With all good wishes.

LISA'S STORY

8 A.M.   5 spoons of cereal, juice

I put on makeup as usual. A little annoyed. I don't think I ever told the rabbi about my eyelashes. Basically (I don't even know if this has got to do with the ED), now I'm missing some of my eyelashes in my left eye so I don't usually leave my bedroom without eyeliner. Otherwise I don't want to say what I look like. (I don't mean my eyelashes are thin. I mean there is quite a big gap.) So this morning I noticed that I think some more of my eyelashes fell out.

It's not easy for me. I'm a girl and especially on Yom Tov, and even more so when it's a 3-day Yom Tov. (Yes, it's hard Shabbos – because you can't put on makeup on Shabbos — but I found an eyeliner that basically lasts. But I get nervous when I sleep in case I rub my eyes and it comes off.) I hope they grow back soon. When they start growing, it takes like 8 months to fully grow back. I used to have missing eyelashes on my right eye, and my left eye was normal, and they grew back finally after a long time. Then I went out with that boy and after he said no, I lost some again. So it's a crazy cycle.

It was interesting about 2 months after I came back from New York, a girl in my class — it was someone popular (who was trying to be nice but this is how it came out) got a little upset and annoyed with me and told me off. She said that I never join them when they go out, and why am I separating myself. Like, what's my problem? The reason was because I felt yuk (this is on top of my ED) because of how I looked (I had not yet discovered the eyeliner I use now) and not only that but I knew girls will ask about my eyelashes and say things like uuuk aghgh. (Some smart girls did pick it up, but at least they didn't ask me out loud so others could hear.) Anyway, after a while, I finally told her the truth. She felt so bad and even though I didn't want to tell any-one — and her especially — it felt good to answer someone back with such a

43

good answer. And trust me, she felt so so bad. I could see on her face and she had nothing to answer or say to me (for a change).

9:30 A.M.   Two pieces of cake and 2 little cheesecakes

10 A.M.   Two fruit roll-ups

Okay, I mucked my day up AGAIN.

I really need to explain things over the phone so it will be clearer. But anyway, I know I'm not going to be hungry tonight but I always force myself to eat some fish, soup and chicken because it's a mitzvah. I know this is my yetzer hara [evil inclination] dressed up as yetzer tov [good inclination] but really what should I do? Can I just eat a small piece of challah and that's good enough?

(I'm not making excuses to eat. I really don't have an urge to eat/binge in front of other people - especially when we're having guests like tonight. I actually don't want to eat and prefer to stay in my room and listen to music or do my own stuff.) By the way, I prefer to eat alone and when it's quiet I feel I can concentrate better, be more relaxed, and stop when I'm full.

Rabbi Goldwasser, I tried to keep a diary religiously and send it off. I know there is no magic but I am craving to get better (and be skinny). Can you please tell me what I can do? And if you think something that I think or am doing is wrong or weird or whatever, please tell me. I have been hurt so much by people. I don't [think I will] care if you tell me something I am doing is wrong. Like some people say - I don't want to tell you because it might offend you.

(Also, I forgot to write in my other e-mail – about listening to a shiur, I think I should take a break from listening to speeches that are not always encouraging. Some even speak about punishment and the effects of actions and things

we do. I take everything so to heart it drives me mad. So I think it's wise to stop for a little bit and focus on recovering. Am I making sense?)

Thank you so so much for everything,

Have a good Shabbos.
Lisa

‌ SHABBOS NIGHT

Dear Lisa:

Hope all is well. I saw that Thursday must have been a very difficult day for you.

Concerning your dizziness: please keep a check on it. It may be a good idea to see a doctor. What happened before 5:00 P.M. that caused you to binge? I was also moved to hear that you felt it's *gehennom*. That comment gives me an indication as to the depth of pain that you feel. Remember though, *gehennom* is temporary, even for someone who's bad and from what I know and understand of you, Lisa, you are a very good person, who is only interested in improving and being close with Hashem. So *gehennom* of any sort is not the place for you. You've got to climb out and know the great good that Hashem has in store for you.

R' Noach of Lechovich said that we must look at life like a discus thrower. When he wants to be able to hurl the discus many, many feet up into the air, he bends down very, very low toward the ground in order to gain maximum momentum. Sometimes when we experience declines in life, it is a descent that will prepare us for future ascent. Regardless of what you have gone through — the pain and the torment — know that at any moment Hashem can raise you up to great heights!

As I followed your letter, I also read about the boiling bath. Please do not use the body as a target. Things like this reinforce negative feelings about oneself, and also give a sense of satisfaction that we are somehow rectifying ourselves by self-inflicted pain. We have to replace the thought process that leads to this type of action. You are deserving of the finest things in life. Your *neshamah* is pure. Each morning, right after you say *Modeh Ani*, you have to say, "I am a good person. I deserve the finest *brachos* [blessings] in life and do not deserve punishment."

There are many good ways to be able to understand and "feel" emotions, thoughts, and feelings. Pain is similar to an addictive substance. The substance may appear to be rectifying the situation for the moment, but in truth it is plunging the person down deeper into the abyss of despair.

On a different note, your comment on the books is, as usual, on target. Even experts need to have understanding and insight into the human condition, in order for their writing or speaking to have any level of quality.

Thank you for sharing with me your concerns about your eyelashes. This is yet another challenge of the whole disorder. I would like to know, however, if there is anything presently that may be the cause.

Concerning lasting makeup for *Yom Tov* or *Shabbos*: there are cosmetic tips available, as well as some other brands on the market, that have been used by people who are unfortunately experiencing this malady. I pray that the situation will be resolved soon, and that the crazy cycle comes to an end. I will talk to you about this more at a later time.

Lisa, about the girl who made a comment to you about why you never come on Shabbos: please understand that they like you and want you to be a part of their groups. They are not asking you in order to make you feel uncomfortable. I believe they want you to know how much they welcome your participation. They may not even notice many of the things that seem to you very conspicuous about your appearance.

We have reviewed some of the Shabbos foods that are *l'kavod Shabbos* [for the honor of Shabbos] and have the extra *segulah* [fortuitous] to them, so whatever you're able to eat is good. Do not force yourself, and do not allow yourself to have negative feelings. I pray for the day that you can truly enjoy the Shabbos foods, as it says in the *zemiros*, "meat, fish and all the delicacies."

Believe me, you are on the road to getting better and to healing. I will definitely be honest with you if there is anything that I feel you are doing is wrong or weird.

Lastly, concerning listening to speeches that upset you: only listen to things that are encouraging. All the talk about punishment and penalties will not help in the least bit. What will help is *divrei chizuk*, encouraging and inspiring words that are full of hope and blessing.

Keep up the good work.

With best regards,
Rabbi Goldwasser

Part One – Friday night

2:30 P.M.   Challah

*6:45 P.M.   After candle lighting before the meal/Kiddush — chocolate
cake, cheesecake*

Shabbos meal — too much challah

I definitely know my trigger this time. I hate when my parents fight.

*Sorry, let me rephrase. My mother says something to my father that's so not
nice and with such an unacceptable tone of voice. My father, a tzaddik, just
sort of does what she wants and tries to pretend everything's OK.*

*Now, we had guests and I felt myself slowly and steadily boil up inside. I was
so embarrassed for myself and of my parents. (Really it has nothing to do with
me. I'm just their daughter; but this is how I feel.) Anyway, I'm not judging
my mother. I'm just putting the facts on the table. She works extremely hard
all week. And, yes, I think my father does, too. So when my mother gets
upset at my father and says, "I worked so hard ... now you get up and take
care of the house" (She didn't say those words but that was the part of the message. It's not important for now what my mother said) — so what does that
mean? My father took a vacation all week?*

*Anyway, this is a topic of its own. All the abuse in my house (between my
mother and father, parents to kids, and us siblings to each other). It's absolutely horrible. I don't think this should be happening in a religious house.*

*I can't forget one night when my younger brother was going through a very
difficult time and was physically fighting with my father — the shouts and*

48

the yelling. It was scary. A lot of the children woke up and we were all petri-
fied. I remember just freezing and standing totally still. I really wanted to
call the police because I was scared someone might get seriously injured (they
are both strong). Finally, my older brother had to go and physically pull them
apart and then my brother left the house.

So again, I really don't mean to judge my parents. They probably went
through stuff, too, but this is my reality. And it's not a case of her fault, your
fault, but I know a lot of this comes from my mother. I just want to make
this point clear since the two examples I brought were about my father. This
is really not the case; for some reason, it's mostly my mother.

(I love my father. He's chilled and listens so well and is understanding.) I re-
member when I was young having such a real, almost tangible fear of my
mother. If I ever stepped out of line a drop, or didn't listen to my mother, she
would hit me hard or embarrass me in public if we were in public.

Okay. I can talk on and on about this, but I'll stop now. It's impossible to ex-
plain 20+ years in one e-mail.

I'm actually actively working on being nonjudgmental toward other people
by thinking the following: Everyone has faults including (especially!!) myself.
(I'm talking straight now and being realistic; it's not my low self-esteem voice
speaking.) Every time someone does something and I feel (obviously don't say
it) like, how could she do something like that? Or I would never do that or I
just can't understand her, etc., I tell myself that just as I do certain things or
certain things are difficult for me or I haven't developed a sensitivity toward a
certain thing — exactly the way it is frustrating for me it is for them. And re-
ally, I feel so much more calm now when these situations arise. I deeply feel
and believe this. This thought has helped me listen to others with total sym-
pathy and just being totally nonjudgmental.

Anyway, back to the challah - I told myself, okay, yes, this happens in my house and it's not comfortable. But I am stronger - my binge is stopping here. (I was obviously in a good mood because of our conversation.)

All I ate after that was one bite of fish, a bowl of soup and one bite of chicken.

Before I went to bed I reread one of the books that I had found amazing. Some paragraphs really spoke to me. I read it and marked those inspiring pages because I want to photocopy them to have, so I can read them every so often for inspiration. (Also I want to return the book before my mother sees it.) By the way, although it is a fantastic book I DON'T recommend it to anyone; the book is so immoral.

Part Two – Shabbos morning

9 A.M. Half an orange

I went to shul. If I would not have waited those extra few minutes for my brother, and then another few minutes to help my sister find her shoe which we couldn't find, I would have arrived on time for the davening. I like being there for that, but I missed it.

But I caught myself and remembered our conversation on Friday, and something I had read, where the author wrote, "I care, but I don't care that much. I care more about my recovery. I've read several books about eating disorders and decided that I'd be an excellent advocate for recovery. I want now, I genuinely want, a full recovery, a full life, a healthy relationship with my body." The author wrote other such things that really hit me hard and made a big impression on me. (This is one quote; I can't copy everything now.)

I felt jealous of her strength and determination. I decided then and there that I am fighting this and succeeding. TODAY I'm not thinking about tomorrow. One day at a time. So TODAY no self-pity, nothing like that. TODAY I'm not standing for it. I will be strong. I am strong. Something so small like food is not getting in my way. I am taking myself seriously. I am tuning in harder to myself, listening to myself and respecting and valuing my own unique needs.

After like 15 minutes, I don't know why but I didn't want to stay in shul. So I left. I went to another shul where I knew there would be no ladies. I davened a little bit and said Tehillim. This shul has about an hour break to learn so I left shortly after and went for a nice, slowish walk for about an hour.

I didn't want to go home. (Shabbos is sometimes hard because I can't just drive off somewhere or listen to my iPod.) I don't like being screamed at or feeling the tension at my house, etc. Shabbos morning I also knew that I might eat before Kiddush because I was a little hungry, but inwardly I wanted to wait for Kiddush.

It worked out amazing. I got home right before my father started Kiddush. I had challah and it was good. Food actually has a better taste when you eat it when you're hungry!

I knew myself. I knew I was going to have tons of challah. I had about 2-3 big pieces and was totally stuffed. Then I had nothing else to eat (besides an anorexic "crumb" of fish for the mitzvah and literally one spoon of cholent).

My grandparents came over after the meal to celebrate my birthday. I didn't have cake.

I felt okay. I definitely overate (because I had a lot of challah) but I'm not calling it a binge.

(I once read that the meaning of the actual word BULIMIA is "eating like an ox". I don't know why, but I like that translation. I think it's a great definition!)

After my Shabbos afternoon nap, I woke up thirsty. I sat down and had a drink of juice SITTING- I'm not bulimic today. I'm acting being normal for one day. Tomorrow I can decide what I will do. I'm drinking from a cup, I told myself, not from the bottle.

I then thought about the fact that even though I told myself that I get upset at Hashem and edgy when I get together with my classmates, and it's rubbed in harder that they're married with children, I still want to prevent those feelings and therefore I don't join my classmates. But really I have a choice:

Have self-pity, feel yuk OR grow up. Be strong. Really, I'm only a stage behind them. Big deal?!! No?

I decided to go and just have fun!!! I went and had such a great time. My friend put on maternity clothes today and it was so much fun sitting around in my friend's house. (She just moved into a new house.) We were talking with everyone about babies and just funny stuff.

Thoughts ... It's a matter of perspective.

(It was really funny. Before I left my friend, my 16-year old sister came into my room and said, "Why don't you wear your new dress? You always wear that" [what I was wearing then].

(I got 3 really nice new dresses for going out. Two I never wore, and the other I wore — I think only once. Anyway, obviously, the reason I never wear them is because I haven't not binged and been my natural size since before Pesach.) I appreciate my sister's concern and her care for how I look (she obviously cares

more than I do!) and the fact that it bothers her that I always happen to wear the same thing for some mysterious reason.

Melava Malka: 1-1/2 slices of challah and fish sauce

Before bed: Apple

When I went to bed I made a conscious decision: My sister is coming home this week. I can act like a baby or have an amazing time with her. She is tons of fun- so smart, helpful and really fun to be with. I am really excited to see her. We can go shop together and go to the beach — I can't wait!

More thoughts:

First day in a long, long time I didn't have cake. It's pretty funny. Yes I can actually do it.

I don't know what will happen tomorrow, what my mood will be, but one thing I know for sure. Whatever I built today can never be destroyed. I can fall from the edifice I built today, but the edifice will always be there forever.

Dear Lisa:

Hope this note finds you well.

I agree with you, most definitely a disruption of *shalom bayis* [domestic harmony] on any level affects **EVERY** member of the family. Each of us feels many different emotions: responsibility, shame or uncertainty that is certainly enough to trigger action, and no one can affect us as deeply as a parent.

Unfortunately, when people trade words they don't always know the far-reaching effect of their words, once they let them out of their mouth. Usually there is a decline that begins with words. As the arguments become more intense, other things happen. Once the floodgates burst, everything breaks loose. It is hard for a young, idealistic woman like yourself to understand it. Just remember, no home is immune. Unfortunately, in today's world, where all the boundaries have been broken, we too suffer from the ills of society. If it weren't so, the thousands of books on parenting and at-risk youth would not be so popular today.

The event that you witnessed on that one night was enough of a nightmare to really haunt a person. I hope and pray that you will be able to work through what you have witnessed and experienced and eventually be able to put it back in the furthest recesses of your memory.

Intervention in today's world is so important, but it takes one who is willing to admit that things are out of control, and that they are ready to begin to accept help. That is a big step, and many people have already become used to the cycle of upset – tension – anger - frustration – disruption – violence – reconciliation – forgiveness - peace.

Who knows what your parents may have experienced in their own lives, and the challenges that the "family" presents to them. They also need a lot of understanding as to their mode of behavior and their reactions.

Concerning the part, in particular, that you experienced as a younger girl: I can only tell you that my heart goes out to you. No one should ever have to experience the "school of hard knocks". When you have time, I would like to discuss it with you by phone. Despite anything that has happened, we achieve what we do in life **NOT IN SPITE** of everything that has happened but sometimes **BECAUSE** of everything that has happened. I have a feeling that you will have great *hatzlacha* [success], and that Hashem has given you the special abilities necessary to persevere.

Concerning self-esteem: it is a lifelong pursuit. I often reiterate that it is important to remember that we were all created in the image of Hashem. I like your method of understanding others with total sympathy and not being judgmental. I am also happy to hear that you are in a good mood. May the good moods come more frequently and last longer.

Don't worry, I will not recommend the book to anyone else, but I am happy that you were able to gain from it. We say in *Tehillim (119:99)*, "From all my teachers I grew wise," but don't forget to be careful with the sources.

Keep up the good work, and as it says (*Yeshayah 40:31*) "Those whose hope is in Hashem will have renewed strength"!

Rabbi Dovid Goldwasser

STARVING SOULS

Dear Lisa:

Hope this note finds you well. I was glad to hear that you went to *shul*. *Bais medrash* can be an oasis of encouragement, hope and healing. Always make it an enjoyable experience. Try to get to the prayer services for the parts that you like. These days, *chizuk* [encouragement and inspiration] doesn't come often, so when there is an opportunity grab it.

I love your quote from the book. I am also very pleased that you are talking about "fighting this and succeeding today, one day at a time." It is just an excellent piece. Interestingly, the Breslover organization put out a very small pamphlet titled, "Only Today." It is a *mussar* thought about living in the present day, succeeding and valuing the time unit of one day. Many people who were not able to be helped by other publications related to this booklet.

It's also good to get out and to walk, observe nature, do whatever you can when you feel like being away from home.

I was happy to hear that your grandparents came over for your birthday. I'm sure that made you happy. Grandparents can have a very special bond with their grandchild.

I can see that you're making headway. Acting normal is great. Drinking from the cup instead of directly from the bottle is great. Your line comparing "self-pity, and feeling yuck" to "growing up and being strong" is definitely going in the right direction. Believe me, it will be no time before you are standing right with your friends, and not staying behind. Friends **are** important. The *mishnah* in *Pirkei Avos (1:6)* tells us, "*Kneh lecha chaver* – acquire a friend for yourself." The literal meaning of the word *"kneh"* is to buy. Our commentaries tell us that even if a person actually needs to buy a friend it is worth it. That's how important a friend is.

Concerning your sister, I think it was very nice that she asked you about what you're wearing. She looks up to you; you're her older sister and she loves you. She wants you to look good, and thinks that you do. Knowing how to accept love is a very big step for many, especially those who are experiencing a challenge.

Congratulations on your first day being "cakeless". Don't worry about tomorrow – "only today". I very much appreciated your words at the end. "I can fall from the edifice I built today, but the edifice will always be there forever." May you constantly spiritually ascend in your life, every day, for 120 years.

Best regards.

9 A.M.   *Compote*

10 A.M.   *Grapes*

I am craving cake or something good.

I ate ice cream. A little later more ice cream, and more ice cream
Then I had an ice cream cone.
I finished the ice cream.

Cake
I finished the cake

2 big bowls of salad - almost chipped my tooth - got so scared
5 or 6 bowls of soup – can't remember
I think that's all -
Oh, a bagel

I don't know a word in the dictionary to describe how I feel. I'm beyond
anger, beyond disappointment and long beyond tears. I feel really deeply –
can't think of the right word. Probably a word so sharp and deep doesn't
exist.

LISA'S STORY

Dear Lisa:

Hoping all is well with you.

Read through your menu. Quite a day!

I can relate to and feel your pain. The words beyond anger, disappointment and tears are *tzaar* and *yagon*. All I can say is that Hashem promises He will gladden us according to the days we were afflicted.

Commensurate with the disappointment, the anger and the upset that you have experienced will be a future of joy and *simcha*, as we say in the Shabbos *zemiros*, "And sorrow and woe will flee."

It is interesting to note we read (*Yeshayah 25:8*) that in the future, "Hashem will wipe the tears from all of our faces." The *Malbim* clarifies this with a beautiful commentary that there are many different types of tears – tears of sadness, and tears of heartbreak, but also tears of happiness. In the future, Hashem will wipe away those tears of sadness. We will no longer have to cry over our pain and anguish and disappointments. At that time the only tear ducts that will be flowing will be the ones that emit tears of joy.

I pray to Hashem, from the depths of my heart, that — commensurate with the tears of sadness that you have cried — there will be tears of happiness flowing at each of your future triumphs and *simchas*.

Rabbi Dovid Goldwasser

✍ TUESDAY

Dear Rabbi Goldwasser,

Thank you for your e-mails.

I didn't write diary entries for the past few days since I ate so much I couldn't remember everything. Anyway, I think you know all the kosher foods available -why should I send a list of them!!?

Lisa

✍ THURSDAY MORNING

Dear Rabbi Goldwasser,

I haven't been sending e-mails since my parents don't like it when I go on the Internet.

I'm doing OK. I felt a little weak and tired today, which doesn't make sense because I slept last night from about 10 P.M. to 7:30 A.M. I think it's because I'm low in iron. (Last time I checked my iron count, it was 21 when it's supposed to be at least 30.) I'm bingeing and only eating bad foods- so therefore I'm probably lacking in a lot of nutrients.

I listen to music a lot and it really helps me relax. Am I allowed to listen in the Three Weeks? (When I asked about listening to music during Sefirah, I was allowed to.) I'm getting very nervous about this.

Thank you so much,
Lisa

✐ THURSDAY AFTERNOON

Dear Lisa:

Hope you're doing better.

I read your latest e-mail in which you said you were feeling a bit weak. Please do go to an MD. You may go alone and the visit will surely be confidential. If you feel you need iron, then there are vitamins that can boost your iron, and some foods that could be helpful to you, i.e., liver, sardines, beans – lima, kidney, lentils — meat and chicken, spinach and asparagus.

Concerning bingeing and eating bad foods: maybe try to include some healthy foods into the mix in order to get more nutritional value. Just a suggestion.

Concerning the music issue: you could listen to music that is inspirational. There is a *heter* [allowance] for you to listen to music that is inspirational. Please do not let yourself to get nervous about this, and we can further discuss this by phone.

The sample suggested menu that we discussed will hopefully be mailed to you a little later today.

Please keep up the good work. May Hashem give you great strength and ability to overcome every challenge.

With best wishes of *bracha,*
Rabbi Dovid Goldwasser

STARVING SOULS

Dear Rabbi Goldwasser,

Both my parents are not home. This doesn't happen often so I'm just sitting down quickly to write how my day went.

Today I overate — naturally, obviously.

Thoughts: I have a sister who is stick-skinny and she eats so so much. How does she do it? Honestly, I can't understand. She doesn't even get bloated. She's so lucky!

This is unbearable
The pain is so agonizing
When will I get better?
Will I ever get better?
It's already six years.

I wish I could lose weight on my body and face, and I wish I could get better and be happily married and have children.

A lot of "wish"s.

I'd better go. I'm supposed to be watching everyone even though I'm in pain. (I fell very badly yesterday.)

Thank you again,
Lisa

LISA'S STORY

 **FRIDAY**

Dear Lisa:

Hope things are improving. You wrote that you overate, naturally and obviously. I just want you to know that I do not take it as an obvious fact that you're going to overeat. Every day I await good news, that maybe this will be the day that you will meet with great success in overcoming these challenges.

About your sister: it is biological. Metabolism plays a great role in how we are affected by food. Please don't ever compare yourself to anyone else. Don't forget, your own perception of your own self-image may be distorted because of the ED. There is no doubt that in time your perception could be altered to see your own "thinness" and to appreciate your own inner and outer beauty.

Lisa, you will get better. Keep your goal in mind. It may not happen as quickly as you want it, but I definitely think that you **WILL** get better, even though you mention that it has been six years. Don't forget that the seventh year is *shemittah,* when we rest – a special year of achievement and holiness, a year of recognition of Hashem's *hashgacha* [Divine Providence] in the world. I pray that this seventh year will be a *shemittah* for good, a time of great healing and good health, a time of positive thinking and forward movement.

Concerning your "wish list:" keep your wish list handy. Pray to Hashem, and your every wish for good could be realized.

Knowing that you're in pain, let the fact that others care so much be somewhat of a comfort to you.

Interestingly, another word for pain is *"nega."* The *seforim* say that the word *"nega"* [Hebrew letters *nun, gimmel, ayin*] can be turned around to *oneg* [pleasure, consisting of the same three letters]. One should never despair. No matter how bad the pain, the situation can turn around to *oneg* – sheer delight.

May it happen for you very soon!

❧ **SUNDAY**

Dear Rabbi Goldwasser,

Hello, how are you?

I didn't write down — and I don't remember — exactly what I ate the last few days, but this was the basic flow.

I did overeat/binge definitely but not too bad. For instance, Friday lunch I only had 2 big pieces of cake, one piece of chocolate mousse cake and the other piece was cheese — at least it was only that. Later in the afternoon I ate a lot more.

Anyway on another note, I am really trying to behave and be kind and generous to myself. It's interesting — the nicer I am to myself, the nicer I am to other people, because I feel an inner calmness. And this really makes it not just a thing of the past but — if it makes sense to say this — to accept this test, leave it behind, but bring the lessons with me, keep them and grow from them.

Another thing I realized — that I feel is so true — is that I can read books, get help, etc., but all the real hard, tough and agonizing work and self-discipline have to come from myself. They can't come from anywhere else; that's the only way it'll work. I can look for support and ask for tips or get inspired from someone else's story, but the real work must be done by no one other than myself.

Thank you for being so supportive and helpful and for the major role that you, Rabbi Goldwasser, are playing in my recovery. Even though the work must come from myself, I feel like I still can't do it without the support.

I hope I will be able to have the strength and self-discipline I need to tackle this.

Lisa

 **TUESDAY**

Dear Lisa:

Hope all is well with you. It was good to hear from you. I am pleased to hear that you are being good.

Being kind and generous to yourself is probably one of the most important efforts that you could work on in this world. You are constantly striving upward, and for every small success that you have, feel proud and let the happiness linger. Remember, we are rewarded even for a good thought, how much more so for a good word and a good deed.

It makes sense that the nicer you are to others, the better that you will feel. As we learn *(Shavuos 39a)* "We are responsible for one another." The more we feel that sense of responsibility and love, not only are we strengthening every other link on the chain, but we are strengthening our own as well.

What you write concerning reading books and getting help, and so forth, is true. The hard work and self-discipline, the determination and willpower, are all from you. As the *mishnah* notes *(Pirkei Avos 1:14)*, "If I am not for myself who will be for me?" It is very well applied here. Even if we have the whole world rooting for us, it still takes our own hard work, our own intellectual and emotional powers to reach higher heights. I hold all the work that you have done and are doing to be very valuable. Few people can really understand the uphill struggle and the amount of toil that is necessary for you. I pray that your hard work and dedication pays off big time. "The reward is in proportion to the exertion and discomfort" *(Pirkei Avos 5:23)* — you certainly deserve a large return.

I am thankful to Hashem Yisborach for any role whatsoever that I may have in your recovery.

I believe in you!

✑THURSDAY

Dear Rabbi Goldwasser,

I don't know what's going on. I am trying hard. I think I'm trying my best, but this is crazy! I'm eating worse than a pig. The voices inside my head are so loud, screaming. This is unbearable! I'm so fat, my face is fat. I hate this!!

What can I do better? I can't deal with myself!

LISA'S STORY

Dear Lisa:

I just received your e-mail.

Please do not get down. You are waging a great war, and you're doing well. You ARE trying very hard! Fighting an ED is like coming up against a giant. They are sometimes ten times more powerful than we are. But with determination, self-sacrifice and perseverance you will be victorious. Just as Dovid HaMelech [King David] overcame Goliath.

Try to quiet those voices. What they are saying is true; it is unbearable. But let's see if we can change those voices to shout instead, "Lisa, you can do it! You've got amazing willpower. You have many merits. And you will never let it get the better of you."

Generally, it's dealt with in Cognitive Behavioral Therapy. Sometimes it is a question of analyzing the various relationships that we have. Support groups are also helpful. Certain individuals may also need treatment for depression or mood disturbances.

I am sure that you look much better than you think you look. Others will see your good characteristics, and not your seeming character flaws.

Please remember, Lisa, if you feel the need, you should not hesitate to call someone locally – anybody you feel you could trust – and reach out for assistance.

There are several things that I would like to suggest to help you deal with yourself. It might also be interesting for you to take a look in the *Rambam's* work, *Hilchos Dei'os*, where the *Rambam* addresses issues of healthy eating and general good health.

If possible, try to call by telephone.

I'm truly upset to hear that you're having such a rough time. My heart goes out to you. Please let me know what I can do.

May you go from strength to strength!

⌒⌒ **FRIDAY**

Thank you for your e-mail.

I read the Rambam. But I am a real idiot and totally out of control. I am angry with Hashem, and I can't stand myself.

I will try to call. Thanks again.

⌒⌒ **FRIDAY AFTERNOON**

Dear Lisa:

Hope all is well.

Whatever you do, don't call yourself an idiot. You are a sparkling personality who has a great soul. Even if it is impossible for you to see yourself this way, I can give you a personal guarantee that it is true. If you feel that things are out of control, we must take steps to get things back under control, as we have discussed in the past: making a plan, contacting someone, getting the encouragement that you need from the right places, treatment.

Please do not be angry with Hashem. It is only because we cannot understand the abundant mercy of Hashem that we sometimes get upset with how we see the world going.

R' Elchonon Wasserman *ztl* tells an unbelievable story to illustrate how one must look at events that happen in life with total *emunah*:

> A person once hired a wagon driver to take him to another city overnight. During the course of the night, as the man slept, he was suddenly thrown to the right side of the carriage and banged his head against the wall. He wondered why the driver was being so reckless.
>
> A half hour later he was thrown to the other side of the carriage, hurting his shoulder. He was getting upset with the wagon driver.
>
> About an hour later the carriage came to a sudden halt and the passenger fell against the back of the carriage. Finally, he called out to the wagon driver, "What's going on over here? Why are you driving without control? I am being hurt all over."
>
> "Wait till tomorrow when we drive back, and I will show you what has happened," answered the driver.
>
> On the return journey, the driver pointed out that when he had swerved to the right, there was a huge cliff on the other side. He had to make a sudden move in order to avoid falling over the edge to certain death.
>
> When he swerved to the left, he had averted a large body of quicksand, which would have totally disabled them if not for his quick action.

When he came to a grinding halt, it was because he had suddenly encountered a huge boulder in the middle of the road that could not be passed. If they would not have stopped, there would have been a fatal accident.

So, too, explained R' Elchonon, we are travelers journeying through *galus*. At times we are thrown to the right and other times we are thrown to the left. We sustain some hard knocks, but it is all for the best. Hashem Yisborach conducts the world and everything that happens in the world is in the special realm of Divine Providence.

R' Elchonon was my rebbi's father, and I feel a particular attachment to this Torah of R' Elchonon. I hope it helps.

Besuros tovos.

∽ SHABBOS NIGHT

Dear Rabbi Goldwasser,

I just want to add to my last e-mail about the Rambam. The Rambam wrote there, if I remember correctly, that it's a sin to overeat. Then why does the traditional Shabbos meal have so many courses? You can't eat everything without overeating. I don't know; I can't understand it.

I am fat. I didn't realize how fat I was till I had to go to a specialist after I fell last week and they took pictures of my back. I was so embarrassed. I must lose weight!!

Also, I'm trying so hard to get better. So firstly, I listen to music to calm myself down, and now I can't listen during the Three Weeks. Lately, I started taking hot baths and soon it's the Nine Days . I don't know what to do with myself. What does Hashem want from me - really? Why can't I be normal and get married. Why aren't any boys working out? Am I so bad? I really am trying. I know it might not look like it, but I am.

I don't know what to do anymore.

✍ SHABBOS NIGHT

Hi, sorry, I just reread the letter and forgot to write something. I'm sort of going on the Internet illegally because my parents don't really let me. So I'm just writing fast; that's why I'm not making so much sense and it's coming in dribs and drabs.

Anyway, you asked is there anything you can do. I was wondering, were you able to get the recording of the ED conference that you spoke at in Manhattan? I'm interested in listening to it or anything on the topic. I know other people have this problem, too, but since I don't really talk to anyone, it's hard to believe it.

Thanks again,
Lisa

LISA'S STORY

Dear Lisa:

Hope this note finds you okay. I read your last set of e-mails and can very well understand the frustration you write about concerning Shabbos and the various sources. A correction: It is not a sin to overeat; it is rather not a recommended practice. Please remember that the Torah considers you to be as holy as anybody else in the world.

The truth is that traditional Shabbos meals do not have to have so many courses. It is because people want to give extra honor to the Shabbos and have a chance to sit with their family, entertain guests, etc. Things may have gotten a little bit out of hand.

When I was a young boy in yeshiva, my parents lived a distance from the yeshiva, so I ate by a rebbi who served the bare minimum. There was a small piece of fish, followed by a few slices of chicken, a spoonful of farfel, and some applesauce, with a small piece of kugel. That was it. In the winter there would be soup served. Believe me, those were some of the most fulfilling *seudos* that I ever ate. So there is no *halachah* [Jewish law] about having gross amounts of food or serving everything under the sun.

Sorry to hear that you took a spill. I hope everything is okay and that you are back to yourself in no time, feeling good and strong.

Concerning the pictures of you: do not be too hard on yourself or the way you look in the pictures. Don't forget that whenever we see pictures of ourselves we are much more critical. We are embarrassed by ourselves. Others may not see anything wrong at all; they think it's a beautiful picture.

It seems that our generation are all experts in seeing the negative.

Concerning music during the Three Weeks and the baths: I would like to speak to you by telephone in order to elucidate the *halachah*.

Hashem only wants for you to try as much as you can to heal, for you are a precious daughter. You are like an only daughter to Hashem, and He thinks about you constantly. You are **NORMAL,** and you will get married. The reason the boys didn't work out so far, is because it was not the time. When it will be the right time it will not be delayed for one more second. You must repeat every day, when you wake up and when you go to sleep, "I am good, I am good, I am good."

I know that you are trying. More important than anything, Hashem knows you are trying. Keep up the good work and never despair.

℘ SUNDAY NIGHT

Dear Lisa:

Hope this note finds you well. I understand your dilemma about the Internet. It is a dangerous weapon, so I can appreciate your difficulty in getting access. If there could be a computer with only e-mail, it would be helpful.

Tomorrow, I will call the center that sponsored the Nefesh Conference to see if I can get a CD recording of the event in which I participated.

Please keep up the good work.

LISA'S STORY

Dear Rabbi Goldwasser,

It's so so hard to have faith. It's so hard to wait so long. When will it be my turn to get married? Why do I have to wait so long? I know it's the worst thing to compare yourself to others — especially your classmates — but why am I left behind? Why am I so different? And weird?

Dear Lisa:

Keep the faith! I know the wait is long. Believe me, your turn will come. Without saying too much, we know that finding a matrimonial match is as difficult as the parting of the Red Sea.

The *Meforshim* [commentaries] explain that when it says in *Tehillim (136:13)*, "To Him who divided the Sea of Reeds into parts," it comes to tell us that the sea was divided into 12 channels. Each of those channels were in the shape of a semi-circle, one inside of each other. As such, the tribe that crossed the sea on the innermost semi-circle-shaped channel had a much shorter trip than the tribe that traversed the outermost semi-circle.

Similarly with *shidduchim:* some have a very short journey to meet their match; others take a little bit longer.

But, as the great Gaon HaRav Elazar Shach said, everyone can rest assured that they will make it to the finish line. I know that it is agonizing to wait, and it is even more difficult to see other classmates – younger/older – getting married. The exact moment of your engagement will be the greatest Divine Providence in the world. You do not have to worry at all. It will happen, and in a split second all of your thoughts concerning this will change.

Can you imagine the person standing behind the barbed wire fence in Auschwitz a day before the liberation? Could he ever have imagined, in a million years, that he would see the light of freedom? Can you imagine the religious prisoners incarcerated under some of the harshest conditions known to modern man? If you would have ever told these people that they would see the free world and ascend to positions of stature, would they ever have believed you? I think yes, because they are people of faith.

The Torah tells us *(Bamidbar 23:24)*, "We are a nation that arises like a lion cub." *Meforshim* explain that even after an extended amount of sleep, the lion cub instantly springs up and lunges.

So, too, we will all see the charmed times in life when we will be successful and we will be able to reach our aspirations, our dreams and our hopes. We never let a prison of bricks and stones and metal bars deter those aspirations. We certainly cannot let our mind be our prison.

We are all different. Your differences, and your unique traits and abilities make you who you are. I have not yet met somebody with an ED who did not have hidden talents and capabilities. It's something innate about the nature of those who are prone to this illness that they are blessed with many gifts from Hashem. Study any random survey of profiles and see for yourself.

I look forward to the day very soon when I will hear the announcement of your engagement.

LISA'S STORY

Breakfast: *Half a roll*

Lunch: *Salad, cake*

Snacks: *More cake*

It's now 4:25 — feel bloated. I'd better go and drink a lot of water. I know it's dangerous but I need to keep my weight down.

I feel numb to what's happening — or at least I'm trying to numb myself. I just don't feel comfortable in my own skin. Always trying to hide.

I wish my older sister gets engaged soon. Me too, but her also, and my other sister too.

I just read how some addicts (mainly referring to alcohol addicts) really and truly are not in control. Therefore, they need outside factors to free them from their addiction. Does that apply to me, too, or is food different? (At times I feel I really can't control myself. I just can't. Honestly, sometimes I am pulled to food like a baby to its mother, screaming, like sirens wailing. I can't describe the intensity of those feelings. It's just pure madness.)

Dear Lisa:

Hope things are going well for you.

I read over your latest menu. Cake definitely is the culprit. Sometimes because it is instantly gratifying, tasty and energy-boosting, we tend to rely on cake as a staple. Is it possible to substitute something that does not have as much sugar in order to eliminate that strong craving for more?

Regarding drinking water: you are correct. It is dangerous. There are other ways to deal with weight issues. I would like to mention that drinking more water than one needs places a burden on the cardiovascular system and the kidneys and can hurt a person's health over the long term. Drinking too much water dilutes the salt in our blood and tissues and is life-threatening. There are no obvious symptoms on a moment-to-moment basis.

The numbness that you want to feel is certainly normal. We want to dissociate from things that are not comfortable for us. And you are 100% right; we **ALL** hide behind many veils in this world.

Regarding addictions: whether people are addicted to alcohol or other substances or behaviors, they are not in control. People with addictions need outside factors to free them from their addiction.

- It is important to have a support system in place that provides positive influences and people who make you feel good about yourself
- Maintaining healthy lifestyle practices, such as getting enough sleep, are essential to good mental and physical health. Eating right sup-

plies the body with energy and helps prevent mood swings. Exercise releases endorphins, which have a positive effect on emotions.
- Building stress management and emotional awareness skills will strengthen your coping mechanisms.
- Identify people, places or things that are triggers so that you can avoid them or be prepared to deal with them.
- Therapy can also provide a solid base to build on to prevent feeling overwhelmed.

Yes, you are correct, it does apply to you and the rest of us. Food is no different. The food issues are really a piercing cry from the depths of our soul for help, understanding, rectification, absolution, recognition, healing, consolation, freedom, validity, and exoneration.

Your description in the last two lines of your letter is surreal. I think it is the perfect time to explore positive options. I will call you later to discuss possible options.

Remember, the darkest part of the night is right before the dawn of the new day.

This evening I will be e-mailing to you the menu that we had discussed.

With all good wishes.

Dear Rabbi Goldwasser,

Thank you so much for your e-mail.

I don't have time to write in detail about the last few days but this was the gist.

After I spoke with you on Tuesday I felt good. I don't know why, but actually I felt really, really good. I felt a little excited and slightly changed. But obviously not changed enough to make positive changes.

I've been eating a lot. An abnormal amount, even though my stomach is full — so full that it hurts. But I still keep eating. It's weird. I'm stuffed, but my mouth is watering and wants more and more. I never seem to be satiated. Maybe I'm just not satiated emotionally, if that makes sense. I mean physically I definitely am – obviously. Often when I eat I'm not even hungry to begin with.

I've also been chewing and spitting out - this is not new but I'm doing it now more often. It's absolutely disgusting. I am put off from myself.

I feel so bad about all my parents' money that I wasted this week on food. It's terrible. I don't know what to do.

LISA'S STORY

Dear Lisa:

I was happy to hear from you. We have to take every good moment and try to hold on to it. The fact that you felt "a little excited and slightly changed" is great. You can never tell when something like that might be the catalyst to make substantial changes.

I was certainly sorry to hear about the different bingeing behaviors. They are all, unfortunately, typical of the challenge. Chewing and spitting out is as much a part of it as anything else.

Reasons for bingeing are:

- Sadness or depression,
- Weak coping ability with emotions such as anger, sadness, boredom, or stress
- Dieting, for instance skipping meals, or having days when a person withholds food
- Some say that metabolism may also affect binge eating

Please do not feel badly. You have to try to get the inspiration and encouragement that you need. You are a very good person who is suffering from something that is a little beyond your control. The way to correct this is by taking all the steps necessary, including the right kind of therapy.

Please let me know your thoughts and what might be troubling you at this time in particular, and I will be able to address it in more detail.

STARVING SOULS

Dear Rabbi Goldwasser,

Thanks for your e-mail.

(By the way, I ate today like there's no tomorrow. I don't feel good. I'm in pain in my stomach and back. I don't know what to do with such a pig.)

OK, so the suggestion was to write my thoughts so I can to learn to cope better. So here's some things that bother me, which I feel a lot but I don't usually voice.

My other sister is coming home soon from England. I'm very excited about seeing her. I haven't seen her since last August, but I'm also very nervous. She drives and I'll have to share the car with her. So what's going to happen when I'm craving something, e.g., ice cream and I need to go and buy a tub NOW and she has the car?

Also there is no room in the house. I already have six people in my room, and honestly my room's a horrible mess. My sister, by nature, is really messy and I don't scream at her about it because she doesn't listen. She says she came to visit for her vacation, and her holiday is just relaxing and not worrying about it. Plus, she's older than me.

So my car is mine — it's clean and my space. Not like in my room. When I woke up, one of my siblings took my slippers because they're playing with them or whatever they're doing and I have to spend time finding them. It's just a no-win situation. I feel like we're living on top of each other and now, more than ever when I'm yearning to recover, I need a little bit of space.

I hate when my mother orders me around - literally. And I hate when she bosses me around and says it as if I owe her something, with that sarcastic tone of voice. Yeah, I know she's stressed from the family and she wants to have more children and she's having a hard time with it, but it has a very bad effect on me. (E.g., I don't think this example justifies the above, but I want to tell you what happened on Friday.)

I didn't work that day, so I was in the car doing errands, taking the kids to their appointments, shopping, etc. all day, without exaggeration. When I come home, I'm first greeted by my younger brother, "Hey, Lisa, you want to maybe help?" Like I was having fun driving around all day and doing nothing.

Then a little later, the electricity went off, so my mother wanted me to go to the neighbor I'm very uncomfortable with, to ask her if we could use her hot plate.

Basically I didn't go. I really really really felt very uncomfortable. So my mother ended up going and she was upset. It doesn't matter what she said, but the message was - you are responsible. Why were you so stubborn?

I am part of the family, so I should pitch in and help, but am I responsible? Like what's going on here? This constantly happens.

Also, if my mother knows how hard it is for the bedrooms to be clean immediately in the morning (all the kids use the rooms a lot), why does she keep making weekly appointments at that time and then always screams about it? My mother claims, "Didn't I warn you last week the rooms had to be clean?"

Oh please! Give me a break! I personally don't make a mess in there, and how do you expect me to control the little kids?

I have to get off the computer now. I have to end, but these are just a few things.

I understand why it's good to write. This is what I believe — when someone feels something is truly unbearable and really a deep aching pain that it hurts so much and it cannot be described, no words are good enough. Then when you go and attempt to describe it, you are limiting what happened to some shallow words. (Okay, maybe some deeper or more intense, but not as deep or intense as it really is.) Then you are sort of taking away a lot of pain of what really was and cutting it down to that.

So it occurred to me when I reread this that it sounds so stupid. But it wasn't like that. I'm just trying to explain something I don't think is possible to explain, so it's narrowing it down like this. It seems stupid and silly, immature happenings.

I don't know, maybe that's the goal - to make it sound to the person affected that what happened wasn't so bad.

Have a good week.

Thank you again.

LISA'S STORY

Dear Lisa:

I hope this note finds you well.

Please remember I am with you in your times of pain.

Firstly, concerning your sister's arrival: look at it positively. You like your sister; you're excited to see her. All will work out, if you make an equitable arrangement to share the car to your mutual satisfaction. If you will crave something, it may be a blessing in disguise if the car is not readily available to you. If your sister's nature is messy, it will be a challenge to accept others for who they are. Each of us has our shortcomings, and when we can overlook shortcomings in others, it develops our character and makes us better people.

I do realize and fully empathize about your not having your space in terms of your car/room/house. Until the awaited day when you will set up your own home, if you don't have the physical space, then you have to try to create your own space in your mind – a kind of spiritual and meta-physical space where you can escape during these times and feel safe.

Dealing with parents is sometimes our greatest challenge in life. Since you are bright, and you are blessed with understanding, you know why your mother may sometimes be stressed and the contributing factors as to why she sometimes speaks to you in a manner that is harsh. Not that it helps, but the understanding alone does provide a way for us to work things through.

In the example that you gave of Friday when you were working the entire day for the family, the comment from your younger sister must have been very hurtful. It is a shame that sometimes the people we love most and feel closest to, hurt us most.

Family situations are a great challenge. Sometimes we are expected to be super-human, and sometimes one of the children — for some reason — bears the brunt of the burden of the family, and it becomes "understood" that it **IS** his or her responsibility.

The reason family therapy has become so popular is because it is now well understood that the challenges of the home are usually not limited to one person but rather are a result of the dynamics of a family interacting at different functional levels. Believe me, you are to be highly commended and respected for what you do for the family. From what I know, you are a daughter, sister and relative anyone would love to have.

I want to speak with you about family dynamics more in detail at a later time.

I don't think the happenings you discussed are stupid, silly or immature. I think the pain is real; I think the anguish is real; and I think that you are a survivor.

I pray for you and want to continue to work with you on the issues. I look forward to the day when total healing will take place and there will be happiness and joy for all the days of your life.

LISA'S STORY

 **MONDAY**

Dear Rabbi Goldwasser,

Hi, I tried to call today but I couldn't get through. I have a few questions.

First, I just remembered your suggestion about looking at the word emunah [faith] as you mentioned a few weeks ago. Is it possible to send the Hebrew letters to me?

The other thing was I would love to speak to someone in my situation just as friends and to share our EDs. Do you know any girl who would be interested? Preferably someone honest and not so shy.

Thank you very much and I will try to call when I can. I wanted to ask something else but it's easier over the phone.

Have a good day.

 **TUESDAY**

Dear Lisa:

Attached is the word *emunah* in Hebrew letters. It does not have to be written on parchment; any paper will do, so you can print out this page and use it.

Keep up the good work – *hatzlacha!*

STARVING SOULS

Dear Rabbi Goldwasser,

Hi, how are you? I hope I didn't wake you up on Thursday night.

Anyway, I wish I could sell my outrageous, disgusting habits. Actually I will happily pay someone to take it from me.

I am totally out of control lately- but the difference is that I'm just spitting everything out. I hope I don't get to the stage of vomiting, only because I know it's very hard to stop.

I feel so so bad for all my parents' money I waste. I hope they forgive me. And I feel bad for emptying the freezer and pantry. The whole situation is terrible. I feel like I can't stop.

Sometimes I'm so nervous and edgy and don't know what to do with myself that I feel like cutting. Yes. Sounds better; no consequences — just slice my wrist. I don't know what- I feel so much pain I can't handle it . I can't change my parents, my siblings, no one. I have to adjust to them. Feel like screaming now.

Please tell me what to do - why am I like this?

LISA'S STORY

Dear Lisa:

I hope things are good for you. Not to worry, you didn't wake me up on Thursday. Please call when you can. If I am up, I will certainly answer the phone.

Your habits are not disgusting. They are difficult, challenging habits. Habits that one day, I am sure, you will overcome. If you can continue from the stage where you are right now, without regressing any further, it will be easier to control the habit and work toward recovery.

I am sure that your parents forgive you for everything. You are not wasting their money on purpose; you are merely driven to utilize the resources that are available to satisfy a need that has gone unaddressed.

Concerning cutting: that is a horse of a different color. Many individuals who exhibit this behavior are experiencing difficult challenges in their life. It becomes a way of releasing their negative emotions or distracting them from their emotional pain. People who cut see this as a way to relieve their inner pain by transferring it to the outside.

The urge to cut might be triggered by:

- Strong feelings that a person is unable to express such as anger, hurt, shame, frustration, or alienation
- A feeling of not "fitting in" or not being understood
- A need to escape a feeling of emptiness because of a loss
- Depression, bipolar disorder, an eating disorder or compulsive behaviors

Please, if you ever think about cutting, you must reach out immediately.

Call me or call a local doctor, counselor, or somebody you feel you can confide in. It is an extremely dangerous, at-risk, behavior. I feel for you and the tremendous pain that you are in, and I pray that you will pass through this period safely and securely.

You are right. You cannot change your parents. You cannot change your siblings. But we can change ourselves. In speaking with you, it is easy to see that you are full of life, personality, enthusiasm and spirit. Make these things work for you. Ask Hashem for extra *siyata d'shmaya* [Divine Assistance].

∽◦**TUESDAY**

Dear Rabbi Goldwasser,

I thought over the idea of working in Kiruv [outreach] with children. It does strike me but I know it's not feasible here right now (because, as I explained, I'm planning to leave town for an extended period). Is it possible to organize such a thing in Israel (for an immediate start after Yom Tov)? Or is there a language barrier? Actually I do know Hebrew, but I'm obviously not fluent like a born Israeli. So I'm wondering if they will take me.

I am really interested in teaching ages 7-11 and I do have experience (not Kiruv but regular teaching). Anyway, it definitely is something I would absolutely love to do, but I don't know if that will work in Israel.

Thank you again for all your help. I really appreciate it.

Lisa

LISA'S STORY

Dear Lisa:

I hope this letter finds you well. I received your latest e-mail. I am happy that you gave some thought to working in Kiruv; I think you would be great. Even till you leave, you might ask at the new organization if they need help organizing it. When you go to Israel, it is certainly an option for you. Language is not a barrier, because there are many people who speak English who are in need of Kiruv in Israel. I think that the organizations could utilize your talents. We will most probably have to wait until you are actually in Israel to begin to explore the possibilities.

The positive thinking is great. Keep it up! We often find that the Talmud prefers to avoid a negative word or description and alternatively presents the person or situation with a positive spin. Such is the power of thinking or speaking in the affirmative. It is also a major step in healing.

With all good wishes.

∞ SHABBOS NIGHT

Dear Rabbi Goldwasser,

I got a ticket to America. I am first going to Chicago and then New York. I will then go to Israel.

I'm worried my hair has gotten thin. I'm actually worried sick. I don't know what to do. I am trying and trying. I feel like a wreck. I'm worried and wish to get married.

On the other hand, I am, thank God, doing well. I lost about 15 pounds in the past week. I feel like someone new. Looking back over the past few years, I'm so happy about basic things that probably other people give no thought to. Example: sleeping pain-free without needing something cold to make the pain more bearable; just simply turning over without aching all over; I can breathe now without difficulty and — I can't explain it — just walking around feeling physically good, (I'm not talking about the emotional side of it), and a lot more things that I don't have time to write now.

I wish I could give a present to everyone who is suffering: a day living like a normal person - without all the (I feel like swearing, but it's not respectful so I won't) crazy, ugly, discomforts of this disorder. Obviously I can't, but it's just some unrealistic thought.

I hope and pray I don't relapse. I feel like I am waking up now from a scary, horrible nightmare.

I'm not making sense now. I don't know what I'm writing. I'm really tired. I have a lot going on in my life — things that are difficult for me and that are hard for me to handle — that in the past made me binge but I dream to recover so I'm trying to control myself.

I wish I could tell you or someone the hard truth about what's really going on in my life now, but I'm always scared that it's Lashon Hora [evil gossip] (obviously it is). I remember learning that the Lashon Hora must have a constructive purpose and you can listen to someone if it makes them feel better. But if I can control myself from telling someone then I save everyone from the sin but will it make me better?

Thank you so much and have a good week,
Lisa

LISA'S STORY

Dear Lisa:

I received your letter of Shabbos night. I am very happy that you were able to arrange a ticket to America. Hopefully, in the brief time that you are here, it will be possible to do some important work to further your good health and welfare.

It was also heartening to hear that you feel good about various things in life. Every once in a while, when we take note of these things, it is a great *mitzvah* – that is accompanied by great reward — to say just a few seconds of thank you to Hashem.

Hair is a barometer of one's overall health. With regard to your thinning hair, it is most often a temporary condition caused by many factors that could be applicable to your particular situation. Extreme emotional or physical stress can cause thinning of the hair; poor dietary habits or disturbed metabolism create a deficiency of the vitamins that are necessary for healthy hair.

I was also moved that even at a time when things are not all rosy for you, you think about giving "a present" to others who are suffering. As you say, as long as you dream of recovering, there is certainly great hope and encouragement that you will make it. As we know, our Sages tell us that in the way we wish to go we will be led to that point. Please keep dreaming.

Concerning the question of *lashon hora*: I would like to discuss the answer to that with you by phone.

With all good wishes for continued success.

Dear Rabbi Goldwasser,

I'm at someone's house now, so I'm typing really fast.

I'm so angry, upset I don't know what. I'm just beside myself. I binged tonight. I'm about 10 pounds heavier than when I woke up today. I am burning mad. I went out tonight and I was screaming like a mad man in the car . I don't know what to do with myself. I can't be like this. What does God want from me? Really what what what???

I am honestly trying. Yes, so I'm the world's biggest fool and I never told my parents, so I have no support. But I can't go on like this. I wish I could get married and be normal. What's up with me?

Now I'm nervous, edgy and physically and emotionally in pain. I wish I could reverse a few hours. I can't take all the pressure. Maybe ice will calm me or some hard candy.

What am I supposed to do? I don't know. I'd better go.

LISA'S STORY

Dear Lisa:

I was a little bit concerned reading your letter of last night. I can tell you that I did think about it a lot.

Anger is an emotional state that can run the gamut from mild irritation to intense rage. You could be angry at a specific person or your anger could be caused by worrying about your personal problems.

There are three ways that you can deal with your angry feelings:

Expressing your angry feelings in an assertive – not aggressive – way by learning how to make clear what your needs are and how to get them met, without hurting others.

Calming down by controlling both your outward behavior and internal responses and letting the feelings recede.

Suppressing your anger by focusing on something positive. This will only be successful if you can redirect or convert the anger into a more constructive behavior. There must be some outward expression, otherwise *chas v'shalom* [God forbid] it can lead to an anger that is turned inward – on yourself.

Sometimes we need to express our emotions in a healthy way – letting off a little steam, walking or running, punching a punching bag. Consider these strategies:

- Simple relaxation tools, such as deep breathing and relaxing imagery, can help calm down angry feelings.

- Learn relaxation techniques
- Yoga-like exercises can relax your muscles and make you feel calmer
- Remind yourself that getting angry is not going to fix anything and won't make you feel better. It will probably make your feel worse.
- Silly humor can help defuse rage.
- Sometimes your immediate surroundings – and the attendant responsibilities and problems — may be causing the anger. Give yourself a break. Take some "personal" time.

You ask, what does Hashem really want from you? Hashem wants you to be successful; Hashem wants you to dream; Hashem wants you to believe in yourself. He feels every moment of your pain and sadness and thinks of you with the greatest love, compassion and mercy.

Your life is precious. You have a lot to accomplish in this world. Think about a bright future.

Postscript:

The glimpses of Lisa's life revealed in the preceding pages so far resemble a roller coaster ride with all the ups and downs, twists and turns. There have been days of great progress and other days that are filled with challenge and disappointment.

However, as with many patients, it is important to recognize that living with an ED is lonely and the patient is often detached from the world at large. To experience an ED and yet remain a part of everyday life is trying in and of itself.

As Lisa strives toward ultimately gaining complete equilibrium, she has taken concrete steps toward attaining appropriate treatment. Lisa accepts her personal difficulties with great faith, wisdom and insight. To be sure, she deserves a tremendous amount of credit for expending the energy and effort to survive day to day.

Predictably, progress is slow but usually steady. The prognosis is certainly good. As with any patient, a positive outlook, acknowledgment of the problem, a willingness to get help, and including a spiritual component in one's life will greatly aid in the process of healing and recovery.

THE WORLD OF EATING DISORDERS

I gazed across my desk at the deeply religious young man sitting in front of me. I had been informed that his lineage was distinguished, and he personally was meticulously observant of the finest nuances of Jewish law. He was highly intelligent and had graduated at the top of his class. One look at his gaunt appearance, though, and it was obvious that this was a very sick young man. I had been told that the doctors had already warned Alexander that he might not live to see the end of another month.

Slowly, in a weak voice, Alexander gave me a brief synopsis of his personal life. Brought up in an insular community, he had a relatively uneventful childhood. During his teenage years in yeshiva, though, he developed some Obsessive Compulsive Disorder (OCD) behaviors concerning the reliability of foods in terms of *kashrus*. As he became more vigilant, fewer foods became acceptable for consumption. Produce and grain products were suspect because of various types of infestation. It was difficult for him to ascertain whether the meat and chicken had been prepared with the strictest adherence to the nth degree of Jewish law.

His behavior reached a point of crisis in the 12th grade, when it was discovered that a food product that had been sold in the community as being kosher was in actuality *treif* (non-kosher). His confidence in his fellowman plummeted, and he doubted others' integrity concerning matters of *kashrus*. To be sure, he was a genuinely sincere and holy individual, but ultimately the variety and types of food that he ate became more and more limited.

He explained, "Rabbi, my stringency is not without grounds. Isn't it true that the laws of *kashrus* differ from all the other laws because the foods that we eat actually become a part of our flesh? The other sins do not become integrated within our bodies."

Alexander was aware that his behavior had begun to exceed the norm, but he could not control it. He offered many rationalizations for his actions. "Isn't it true," he said, "that when Moshe went up to *Shamayim* [the Heavens] to receive the Torah he fasted for 40 days and nights? Isn't it true that when the Jewish people were in the desert they ate only *mohn* [manna], and they were a sanctified nation? Didn't R' Tzadok fast for 40 years so that Yerushalayim should not be destroyed? I too aspire to such exaltedness and holiness."

I replied that there is a great difference between Moshe Rabbeinu and all the rest of us.

But he retorted, "Doesn't it say that everyone has the ability to be as great as Moshe Rabbeinu?"

We spoke at great length, engaging in a deep philosophical discussion of the Torah perspective. Alexander was so sincere in his commitment to live life according to Torah that he had unfortunately fallen victim to a way of life that was literally robbing him of his health.

Suddenly Alexander said, "Could I put my head down on the desk? I no longer have the strength to hold up my head." I became uneasy about his well-being and inquired whether I should call for help.

He declined my offer. "No need to call," he said. "I've been like this for a while. There is nothing unusual about this."

We talked some more, and Alexander began to divulge additional tidbits of information. His self-esteem was very unhealthy; he felt inadequate. He believed he was falling short of his religious commitment as a Jew and therefore had a need to do *teshuvah* by being rigorous in his adherence to the laws of *kashrus*.

There was no doubt in my mind that Alexander was in desperate need of intensive counseling and cognitive behavioral therapy. But I did have one thought to share with him.

I asked Alexander, "When you recite the *Kiddush,* what do you think of when you say, '*v'osanu kidashta* – You, Hashem, made us holy'?"

Alexander was well-versed in the concept of the *kedusha* (holiness) of each individual. He knew that every person is imbued with a pure soul from God. His discourse was, in fact, enlightening and very encouraging.

"So," I said, "according to you, each of us already possesses a great holiness." We then delved into a passage in the Talmud *(Gittin 2b)* that discusses the reliability of an individual in matters of *halachah*. I felt that this eloquently expressed a point I wanted to bring home. I concluded by positing that perhaps his inability to perceive his own faithfulness to God was the source of his aspersion on the reliability of others.

He slowly lifted his head from the desk, and a small smile flitted across his face. I noticed a glimmer in his eyes. "Is it possible," he wondered aloud, "that we could meet again to further explore this line of reasoning?"

He heaved a sigh of relief when I agreed, and asked, "Do you think there is any hope?"

"I don't **THINK** there's hope," I responded confidently. "I **KNOW** there's hope."

The progress was slow, but we maintained close contact. As part of Alexander's therapy, I had suggested that he work with one of the respectable kosher certification agencies in the supervision of the manufacturing of food products. This, too, was effective in the healing process, helping Alexander to focus on regaining trust in others.

WHAT IS ANOREXIA (ANOREXIA NERVOSA)?

Anorexia is self-imposed starvation. It is a serious and life-threatening disorder, which usually is caused by underlying emotional stress. Anorexia can cause severe medical problems, including hair loss, endocrinological irregularities, electrolyte disturbances, gastrointestinal problems, neurological complications, and cardiac failure. It can even, God forbid, lead to death. People with anorexia are obsessed with food; however, they will deny their hunger. Some anorexics limit or restrict other aspects of their lives, in addition to food.

The following are some of the common warning signs that indicate that a person may be suffering from anorexia:

- Is thin and continues to get thinner, losing 15% and upwards of his ideal body weight
- Diets or restricts foods, even though he is not overweight
- Is preoccupied with food, calories and nutrition
- Exercises obsessively
- Constantly weighs him or herself
- Has a distorted body image
- Complains about feeling bloated or nauseous, even when eating less than normal amounts of food
- Feels cold and needs to dress warmly, even in mild temperatures
- Has thinning or loss of hair

WHAT IS BULIMIA (BULIMIA NERVOSA)?

Bulimia is a repeated cycle of out-of-control eating followed by some sort of purging. Bulimia is a serious eating disorder that can, God forbid, be fatal. The purging may be accomplished by self-induced vomiting, excessive use of laxatives or diuretics, or obsessive exercising. People with bulimia often feel out of control in other areas of life, besides food. Bulimia can have serious medical consequences including dental and esophageal problems, kidney damage, chemical imbalance, and loss of energy and vitality.

The following are some of the common warning signs that indicate that a person may be suffering from bulimia:

- Often engages in binge eating
- Uses the bathroom frequently during and after meals
- Reacts to stress by overeating
- Cannot voluntarily stop eating
- Is constantly concerned about eating
- Feels guilty or ashamed about eating
- Experiences fluctuations in weight
- Has swollen glands
- Has mood swings or depression
- Feels out of control

Can You Read My Mind?

Anorexia and bulimia can sometimes reflect one or more of the following:

- Inner needs
- Anxiety and guilt associated with separation
- Shame associated with looks
- Lack of self-esteem
- Depression/disappointment
- Feelings of powerlessness
- Abuse
- Lack of control
- Resentment/anger

An Ounce Of Prevention ...

- Constantly develop communication skills with children.
- Do all that is possible to alleviate pressure at home and in school.
- Work on eliminating various forms of competition both at home and in school.
- Never compare siblings or students.
- Allow children to express themselves and encourage them to talk about their hopes and fears.
- Do not stifle children or act in an overpowering manner.
- Learn how to detect early warning signs of various forms of abuse.
- Do not constantly weigh your children or talk about food and weight issues.
- Apologize when necessary.
- Pray for understanding, success, and good health.

WHAT IS BINGE EATING DISORDER?

Binge eating disorder entails repeated and/or frequent episodes of eating unusually large amounts of food in a short period of time, coincidental with a feeling of being unable to control this behavior. Binge eating symptoms may also present in people with bulimia nervosa and affect women only slightly more than men. Outwardly it seems similar to compulsive overeating, but these disorders are motivated by different forces. Compulsive overeaters fantasize about food; people with a binge eating disorder actually have negative feelings about food. Binge eating disorder is an expressive illness, communicating a deeper psychological need or challenge.

People with binge eating disorder may initially become ill because of a lack of proper nutrition; they tend to binge on foods high in sugar and salt but low in nutrients. People who binge often gain weight which could lead to obesity and increase their risk of developing various health problems, such as Type II diabetes, high blood pressure, high cholesterol, gallbladder disease, and heart disease.

Bingeing may be triggered by:

- Depression – almost 50% of bingers are either depressed or were depressed in the past
- Dieting, i.e., skipping meals, not eating enough food each day, or avoiding certain kinds of foods
- Anger, sadness, boredom, worries, stress

The following are some signs that may indicate that a person is suffering from binge eating disorder:

- Eats more quickly than usual during episodes
- Eats until he is uncomfortably full

- Eats when she is not hungry
- Eats alone because of embarrassment
- Feels disgusted, depressed or guilty after overeating

WHAT IS COMPULSIVE OVEREATING?

The *Talmud* states *(Gittin 70a)*, "If your meal gives you pleasure, take your hand away from it and do not overindulge." Rabbi Shlomo Zalman Braun[1] notes that the Talmud doesn't say that one should leave the table, rather that he should take away his hand. Rabbi Braun explains that one should not keep on rapidly spooning the food in his mouth, but he should practice restraint, partaking of his food with forethought and good sense.

The Chazon Ish once remarked to a colleague that he felt absolutely no different before ingesting food or after eating. If he was presented with food by family members he assumed that he had not yet eaten his meal.[2]

The Rambam *(Hilchos Dei'os 4:15)* notes that many illnesses are brought on by eating foods that are harmful for one's health or because one has gorged oneself, even on healthy food.

These principles are, of course, supported in *Proverbs (21:23)* where King Solomon writes, *"Shomer piv ul'shono shomer mitzaros nafsho* — one who guards his mouth and tongue guards his soul from troubles." Our Sages explain this to mean that if a person guards his mouth from eating foods that are not good, or from overindulging, and guards his tongue from speaking improperly, he will be shielded from distress and anguish.

The Rambam notes in his writings that a physician who is concerned about his patient's health and well-being should be exacting about the patient's diet. He asserts[3] that overindulgence in food and drink can negatively affect a person's behaviors and character traits.

---

[1] *Shaar Metzuyanim B'Halacha*
[2] *Sefer Pe'er HaDor*, Volume 3
[3] *Shemone Perakim*

Eating nourishes the body and is generally a pleasurable and satisfying experience that is a natural part of our lives, as we learn in *Ecclesiastes (9:7)*, "Go and eat your bread with joy ..." In fact, food is an important element in many events and special occasions, including *Shabbos* and *Yom Tov*. Many of us have sometimes even experienced the feeling of having eaten more than we should have.

Studies now seem to indicate that compulsive overeating is driven by a food addiction. It is similar to other substance dependencies, and people who are addicted to food tend to mimic the characteristics of those with other addictive behaviors.

By and large, such people tend to be overweight, although "normal weight" people can have this problem as well. They are usually aware that their eating is out of control, but they need the food to fill an internal void and to help them cope with daily stresses in their lives.

Pressures of work, a lack of energy, feelings of boredom or loneliness can often upset an otherwise well-adjusted lifestyle. In this context, people turn to food for comfort to avoid or suppress negative emotions, or to fill a need for affection. It leaves one with a feeling of numbness which disassociates him/her from his feelings.

Compulsive overeaters consistently eat without control, followed by intense feelings of shame about their behavior and its effects (real or perceived) on their body image. Issues of powerlessness, guilt and failure are common among individuals with a food addiction. The more weight they gain, the harder they try to diet. They become obsessed with weight loss, instead of focusing on the cause of their weight gain – the compulsive overeating. The deprivation of the foods they enjoy creates a stronger craving for them, and that usually leads to more overeating. This develops into a repetitive tormented cycle of negative feelings that are soothed with food. The suffering individual becomes entangled in a war with his/her own body.

There is an incontrovertible connection between human emotions, the brain and the stomach. As with all eating disorders, a common component is the presence of low self-esteem. Our society has fostered an attitude that associates one's inherent worth with control of one's weight. The reverse – failure — results in self-censure and feelings of humiliation.

It should be noted, as well, that new research is indicating that a constant pattern of overeating stimulates a normally dormant metabolic response in the hypothalamus region of the brain. The reaction causes increased levels of overeating, generating a vicious cycle that becomes difficult to break.

Common warning signs of compulsive eating include:

- Eating large amounts of food when not physically hungry
- Eating rapidly
- Eating until feeling uncomfortably full
- Eating alone
- Feeling depressed, disgusted or guilty after overeating
- May have a history of marked weight fluctuations

Instead of simply going on a diet, compulsive overeaters need to address their detrimental relationship with food by

- Modifying eating patterns and lifestyle
- Avoiding situations or foods that trigger overeating
- Learning stress management techniques
- Building self-esteem and interpersonal skills
- Developing hobbies and interests that do not focus on food

PLEASE NOTE:

It is important to point out that weight gain and/or increased hunger may sometimes be attributable to other medical factors not related to an eating disorder.

The glands of the endocrine system, and the hormones they release, impact on one's weight and metabolism. For example, an overactive thyroid can speed up the body's metabolism simultaneously generating an increased appetite. An underactive thyroid (hypothyroidism) often causes weight gain, despite the fact that the individual is eating less and doing more.

Stress causes the kidneys to release cortisol which the body needs for quick and easy energy. However, it simultaneously causes insulin to be released, which results in retained fat in the body, or more weight.

In addition, some medications, such as antidepressants and steroids, are known to stimulate the appetite or lead to unexplained weight gain.

WHAT IS OBESITY?

The Torah relates *(Bereishis, 3)* that Adam sinned and, contrary to the command of Hashem, partook of the fruit from the *eitz hada'as* (Tree of Knowledge). In his explanation for succumbing to temptation, Adam states, "The woman whom You gave to be with me – she gave me of the tree, and I eat."

Rav Abba bar Kahana (Midrashic sage) notes that Adam didn't say "I ate" (in the past tense), but used the present tense, "I eat," meaning, "I have eaten from the forbidden fruit and I will continue to eat."

The Kotzker Rebbe remarks on the ostensible arrogance of Adam toward his Creator. It would be comparable to someone caught stealing red-handed who argues, "I stole this, but I will continue to steal from others."

The Kotzker explains that Adam's defense was actually a statement that reflected a deeper insight into his own psyche. Adam was able to identify his own vulnerability and weakness; he was aware that he was totally under the influence of the Evil Inclination. He understood that at this point in time it was probable that he would repeat his transgression and eat from the forbidden fruit again.

Often a person will rationalize and minimize his wrongdoings, even to himself. Once behaviors and conduct have become habitual they are difficult to change. It is easier to steer clear of any introspection than to contemplate one's actions and consider their implications.

An individual who has engaged in soul-searching and achieved a sense of self-awareness will ultimately succeed. Understanding our own nature, abilities and limitations, and having insight into our personality and individuality are crucial for the development of character. They are powerful catalysts for change.

Obesity, which has reached epidemic proportions in the United States and is a rapidly increasing trend throughout the world, is a chronic condition that is defined by an excess amount of body fat. The general consensus to date indicates that obesity should be classified as an eating disorder and attention should be focused on prevention.

Practically all disordered eating begins with a diet, that is, someone is dissatisfied with his or her body. The furious cycle of eating disorders seems to be sustained by the mixed messages about food and weight that are propagated by mass media, family and peers. On the one hand, society idolizes and admires thinness and shuns obesity. Yet high-calorie foods and rich, high-fat desserts are an essential component in family get-togethers, parties and outings. Thus begins the self-destructive thought process that leads to behaviors and attitudes resulting in the range of eating disorders. From the anorexic who obsessively counts every calorie, to the binge eater who keeps eating because he or she believes "the battle is already lost," the progression from one problem to another is often triggered by a weight-related problem.

Behavior and environment play major roles in causing people to be overweight and obese. Unquestionably, increased food intake, consumption of unhealthy foods, and lack of physical activity are the foremost factors contributing to obesity.

• A diet high in fat or simple carbohydrates leads to weight gain.

Fast foods and fried foods have a disproportionately high number of calories. Consequently, the person consuming these foods is taking in an inordinate amount of calories in order to feel full. Simple carbohydrates (refined and processed foods, wine, beer) are more rapidly absorbed into the bloodstream than complex carbohydrates (fruits, vegetables and whole grains), increasing the likelihood that the sugar will be converted to fat. Moreover, research indicates that, calorie for calorie, complex carbohydrates are more filling and the calories add up more slowly, compared to simple carbohydrates.

• Physical inactivity leads to weight gain

There is a close correlation between calorie intake and energy expenditure. In order to avoid weight gain, physical activity must be increased relative to the amount of calories the person is consuming. Sedentary people burn, or metabolize, fewer calories than people who are active. In addition, muscle is metabolically more active than fat and figures prominently in weight loss. Since women have less muscle than men, they have a slower metabolism than men. Weight training is, therefore, often recommended for women to build muscle.

• Depression, anxiety and other mood disorders are linked with obesity.

Research actually suggests a two-way link between obesity and depression: People who are obese may be more likely to become depressed, and people who are depressed may be more likely to become obese. For some people, emotions affect eating habits. They eat excessively in response to boredom, sadness, stress or anger. Additionally, as a result of their depression, they have more difficulty adhering to an exercise regimen or maintaining good eating practices. People who are obese may be more likely to become depressed because they are displeased with their appearance.

• Medications and diseases may promote weight gain.

Certain antidepressants, anticonvulsants, antihistamines and diabetes medications are associated with excessive weight gain. Diseases such as hypothyroidism or insulin resistance are also known to contribute to obesity.

Very often, obese individuals are convinced to embark on a demanding diet in order to reach the "ideal body weight." However, the treatment of obesity cannot be a short-term "fix." Obesity treatment needs to promote a healthy lifestyle over the course of a lifetime in order to achieve a "healthier weight". Extensive research indicates that even a modest weight loss can result in significant health gains.

WHAT IS ANOREXIA ATHLETICA?

The Rambam (1135-1204) combined his Jewish knowledge with distinction in many areas, including medicine, and was renowned as the court physician in Egypt. In *Hilchos Dei'os (4:14)* the Rambam states an important principle concerning the body's health. He notes that as long as a person makes an effort to do exercise, doesn't overeat, and maintains a healthy digestive system he will not become ill and he will be invigorated, even if he eats deleterious foods.

The *Mishnah* in *Pirkei Avos* (5:20) asserts, "Be bold as a leopard, light as an eagle, swift as a deer, and strong as a lion, to carry out the will of your Father in Heaven." The *gemara (Kesubos 111a)* quotes R' Yochanan concerning appropriate exercise: "One should not sit too long; one should not stand too long; and one should not walk too much because excessive walking is harmful to the eyes."

We find that the Torah guides us in every area of life; exercise is no exception. Indeed, it is an important component of the *mitzvah* of guarding our well-being. As R' Yochanan directs, exercise is good in moderation.

The Brisker Rav once went walking with his son-in-law, R' Michel Feinstein, after the Kol Nidre services on Yom Kippur eve.

Deferentially, R' Michel asked the Rav, "Is it proper to take a walk now on this awesome and holy day, when we have just concluded the Kol Nidre prayer?"

The Brisker Rav responded, "You have never asked this question any other day when we walk. If it is not good to take walks, then we should not be doing so any day of the year. You know, however, that the doctor told me to take these walks for my health. So why should Yom Kippur be different than any other day of the year?"

A new development that has been observed in the area of eating disorders is a rise in the number of people with exercise or activity disorder, also known as anorexia athletica. This is characterized by an addiction to exercise, when the individual no longer enjoys the activity but feels obligated to perform it. It is usually accompanied by at least one unhealthy method of weight control such as purging, fasting, or using laxatives. As with disordered eating, the ostensible goal of the exercise is to burn calories and lose weight. Ultimately, however, the exercise addict feels compelled to work out and struggles with guilt and anxiety if he or she does not do so.

Although compulsive exercising does not necessarily accompany an eating disorder, it is often a comorbid condition. A person with bulimia may exercise to compensate for binge eating. On the other hand, as the anorexic's workouts increase, there may be a continuous decrease in the amount of food he or she eats. An exercise disorder is defined by its extreme nature. The behavior goes beyond the requirements of good health and well-being, and has detrimental results. Individuals who engage in this behavior continue to over-exercise despite injury, exhaustion, and/or medical complications.

Those who compulsively exercise usually do so to feel more in control of their lives. By following a strict workout regimen, they boost their feeling of self-respect. They feel empowered to better cope with their low self-esteem, while simultaneously relieving the guilt and pressure of built-up stressors.

Symptoms of anorexia athletica include:

- Engages in strenuous physical activity to the point that it is unsafe and unhealthy
- An intense, driven quality to the activity where the over-exerciser is constantly preoccupied with his/her weight and exercise routine
- Will not skip a workout, even if tired, sick or injured
- Seems anxious or guilty when missing even one workout
- Doesn't seem to really enjoy exercise sessions, but feels obligated to do them

- Would rather exercise than spend time with friends/family, attend social events, and even misses work or important appointments in order to be able to work out

Physical risks associated with anorexia athletica include:

- Dehydration
- Insomnia
- Depression
- Fatigue
- Muscular and skeletal injuries

THE WORLD OF EATING DISORDERS

WHAT IS ORTHOREXIA NERVOSA?

In discussing the laws of the *nazir* (one who has accepted upon himself a period of abstinence from drinking wine and cutting his hair), the Torah commands him to bring a special *korban chatas* (sin offering) upon the conclusion of his period of abstinence.

The question is asked: Why does he have to bring a sin offering? It would seem that such a person should be commended, for he sacrificed his personal pleasure for the sake of his Creator!

Rashi quotes the Talmud *(Nazir 19a)* that he inflicted pain by abstaining from wine. The *gemara* explains further that when we abstain from physical pleasure, we are denying ourselves a God-given gift. That is the sin of the *nazir*. Although he has dedicated himself to the fulfillment of a vow to abstain, which is a great *mitzvah*, he sinned by – in essence – refusing Hashem's gift. Therefore he is required to bring a sin offering.

The Jerusalem Talmud states *(Kiddushin 4:12):* R' Chizkiyah said in the name of Rav that in the future man will have to give an accounting for everything that his eye saw from which he didn't eat. The Amora, Reb Lazar, made certain to partake of every fruit once every year. The Torah tells us in *Bereishis* that Hashem saw that all He had created was very good. Thus, it is improper for a person to reject Hashem's bountiful blessings.

The emergence of an eating disorder that focuses excessively on consuming only healthy foods is a disturbing new development. Categorized as orthorexia nervosa, it is an obsession with the quality of foods that one eats, as opposed to anorexia nervosa which is an obsession with the quantity of food that one eats. Whereas the anoretic is fixated on losing weight, the orthorexic is motivated by a desire to feel healthy, natural and "pure."

Orthorexia nervosa may have a common psychological characteristic associated with obsessive-compulsive disorder, but it is an illness in and of itself. Orthorexia nervosa often begins as a simple quest to eat in a healthy way or to treat a specific allergy or ailment, but then escalates out of control. The individual becomes totally preoccupied with a self-imposed dietary regimen that eliminates all foods that contain fat, sugar, animal products, or chemicals, are preserved; or include artificial, i.e. not natural, ingredients.

Usually, orthorexia is merely a source of psychological distress. However, emaciation and malnutrition are often a result of the severe limitations of the diet, reaching the extreme condition seen in anorexic patients, and can even lead to death.

Signs and symptoms (persisting as a long-term behavior pattern) include:

- Individual spends more than three hours a day thinking about healthy food
- Has feelings of guilt and self-loathing when the diet is broken
- Gives up foods that were enjoyable in order to eat the "right" foods
- The nutritional value of the meal is more important than the pleasure of eating it
- Becomes socially isolated in order to eat healthy
- Orthorexic feels more virtuous and superior than others who don't eat healthy
- Orthorexic feels in total control when strictly adhering to the diet

THE WORLD OF EATING DISORDERS

WHAT IS NIGHT EATING SYNDROME?

Before we begin the Seder on the night of Pesach, we recite the sequence of the entire night's proceedings, from beginning to end.

The commentaries ask: Why do we have to outline in advance what we will be doing? As we read the Haggadah we will be directed to each stage of the proceedings of the Seder.

Our Sages tell us that this teaches us the major importance of orderliness. A person's life must be conducted methodically and with a sense of organization. One of the aspects of adhering to a schedule is eating meals at appropriate times during the day, as is the way of man, unlike disordered eating when one consumes food, or his meal, at irregular times.

This is similar to the concept expressed in *Ecclesiastes (Koheles 3:1)*, "*Lakol zeman v'es* – there is a time for everything." The great sage Rabbi Yisroel Meir HaKohen, known as the Chofetz Chaim, expounds: "There is a time to learn, a time to sleep, and a time to eat."

Night Eating Syndrome (NES) is primarily identified by a pattern of late-night binge eating that continues for two months or more. It is characterized by a lack of appetite in the morning and overeating at night. The person consumes fewer than usual calories during the day and late-night binges almost always consist of carbohydrates. Individuals presenting with this disorder usually express an uncontrollable desire to eat at night, similar to an addiction. It is a clinical illness characterized by changes in hormone levels related to sleep, hunger and stress. Although it can affect all ages and both sexes, it is more common in young women.

Signs and symptoms include:

- Individual generally has trouble falling asleep or staying asleep

- Wakes frequently and then often eats foods that are carbohydrates, starchy and/or sugary
- Suffers from depression or anxiety
- Night-eating episodes evoke feelings of guilt rather than pleasure or enjoyment
- Skips breakfast and doesn't eat for several hours after waking
- Consumes at least half of his/her daily caloric intake after dinner

THE WORLD OF EATING DISORDERS

WHAT IS MANOREXIA?

The Torah tells us (*Devarim 4:15*) "*V'nishmartem me'od l'nafshoseichem* – take great heed with your souls." This commandment is incumbent upon all members of the Jewish people – men, women, great *tzaddikim* and ordinary people.

Rabbi Ze'ev Edelman recounted the following incident:

> The great Torah sage R' Chaim of Brisk (1853-1918) was encountering some resistance with his son, Velvel. He was an extremely thin young boy who ate sparingly, much less than other boys his age.
>
> Velvel once accompanied his father on a trip to Radin to visit the great Chofetz Chaim, Rabbi Yisroel Meir HaKohen Kagan.
>
> R' Chaim of Brisk said to the Chofetz Chaim, "You are one who can relate to everyone. Could you try to influence my son not to avoid his meals?"
>
> The Chofetz Chaim turned to the son of R' Chaim. "Velvel," he said, "the Torah is broader than the oceans. If you want to thrive in your learning it requires great strength, as the *mishnah* tells us in *Pirkei Avos* [3:17], 'If there is no flour there is no Torah.'"

For many years, eating disorders have been regarded as a woman's problem. However, the results of a Harvard study, conducted in 2007, provided conclusive evidence that the illness is increasingly affecting males. To be exact, 25% of people with anorexia or bulimia and 40% of binge eaters are men.

It was long thought that only impressionable young girls were vulnerable to the media's preoccupation with excessively thin images and pop culture personalities. However, today media messages are increasingly directed at males. Touting dieting and ideals of muscularity, this emphasis on male body shape, size and physical appearance is a factor in the rising number of males with eating disorders.

While in the past men did not give much thought to their bodies, as long as they were strong enough to do the necessary work, society's obsession with looks and the cultural emphasis on physical appearances are producing feelings of inadequacy among many vulnerable boys and young men.

Recently, the media has coined the term "manorexia" to refer to male anorexics, although it is not an officially recognized medical term. The symptoms of anorexia and bulimia are the same in men and women. However the underlying issues of self-esteem vary significantly between the two genders.

Studies indicate that men with eating disorders have had negative reactions to their bodies from their peers while growing up. Research also suggests that male anorexics tend to be socially inhibited, less aggressive physically, less competitive and more dependent.

Whether it is overall societal pressure that sets unrealistic standards, or athletic or academic demands, the pressures felt by maturing teenagers often magnify their insecurities, and precipitate the full-blown development of an eating disorder in males. Often, male anorexics were overweight as young boys and teased about it, or they failed in their attempts to excel in athletics. Whereas girls are generally younger when they become anorexic because they fear becoming overweight in the first place, men may often have been overweight as a child and then become fixated on building the perfect male physique by dangerously restricting their caloric intake and/or becoming obsessed with exercise.

Because disordered eating has long been classified as an illness of women, men are especially reluctant to divulge this problem. They perceive the acknowledgment as stripping them of their manhood, and it is almost demeaning to them to admit that they have been brought to their knees by food.

Pediatricians, coaches and parents of boys often have difficulty recognizing the problem, although boys are just as much at risk as girls are.

Because the underlying causes of eating disorders in males differ from those that lead to the problem in women, the treatment needs to address the specific emotional factors unique to the men.

Unlike girls and women, boys are more reticent to talk about their bodies. Yet their unrealistic expectations and visions of the "ideal body image" must be addressed, as noted below:

- Parents must be aware that boys may be as susceptible as girls to developing an eating disorder. Radical and obsessive workout sessions, extreme changes in eating habits, sudden weight loss and increased muscle growth may signal the onset of an eating disorder.
- Call attention to the fact that very few men in real life look like society's projection of the ideal physique. Bodies come in all different sizes and shapes and each of us is a unique individual.
- Help children focus on developing their particular talents and potential, rather than focusing on their physical body as a measure of their worth as a person.
- Model healthy regular eating. Do not fixate on weight issues or trying to maintain a "fat-free" zone in your home.
- Discuss your kids' friends, since boys will usually talk more freely about others than about themselves. Find out whether any of your son's "friends" are engaging in disordered eating and how your son feels about it.

WHAT IS SENIOREXIA?

The Torah tells us *(Vayikra 19:32)*, *"Mipnei seivah takum* – You shall rise in the presence of an old person." Our commentaries explain that this is not limited to the physical act of standing up for people who are old and according them honor. Also our thinking, our attitude and our demeanor should be steeped in reverence and respect for the elderly.

Although much of the recent publicity about eating disorders focuses on anorexia nervosa among teenagers and young people, the latest research seems to indicate that there is a rising occurrence of this illness among the elderly population. It is currently being reported that elderly men and women suffer from eating disorders more often than is generally realized.

While the main cause of anorexia among teenagers centers on the teen's poor self-image, the causes of this illness among the elderly population may include more than a psychological/emotional component.

It is believed that the onset of anorexia nervosa in all age groups is often triggered by a major stressful event. In older people, the loss of a relative and a limited number of meaningful relationships, or retirement leading to a lack of enthusiasm for life and/or depression, may set the illness in motion.

Many elderly people live alone with a limited social network, making it more difficult for others to identify their eating disorder behaviors. Some members of the aging population with inadequate financial resources restrict their food intake to cut back on their grocery bills. It has also been found that age-associated impairment of taste and smell, or the effects of certain medications, negatively impact the choice and quantity of food that the older people consume. Ultimately, there is diminished appetite, with the patient refraining from eating and repudiating hunger. It is accompanied by a distorted perception of body image; the patients do not consider themselves thin, even though they may have become emaciated.

Nurses tell of patients in their care who refuse food with typical excuses such as, "I'm full," or "I don't feel well." Often the only food they actually accept is a glass of milk. At other times it is a gradual process of diminished food intake, which the professionals fail to notice until it is too late. Such older people may be crying out for the attention of relatives or loved ones, and expressing their distress about confinement in a nursing home or their restricted visitations/activities. For some, the sense of despondency and dejection is so overwhelming that they engage in passive suicidal behavior.

In essence, the primary reason for an eating disorder at any age – including the elderly – is the need to gain control over one aspect of life, whatever facet that may be.

A parallel expression of despondency in the elderly is noted in the narrative concerning Barzillai of Gilad (*Shmuel II,* 19:35–41). Barzillai, a wealthy man and a loyal ally of King David, supports the king during the time of Avshalom's rebellion. When King David finally returns to Jerusalem to reclaim the throne, he offers to reward Barzillai for his faithfulness. Barzillai, who is eighty years old, protests and says, "How many are the days remaining of the years of my life . . . does your servant taste what I eat or what I drink?"

Indeed, our Sages acknowledge the infirmities of age in detailing the Torah's mandate to honor one's parents. The Shulchan Aruch (*Yoreh Dei'ah* 240:10) observes that, even in the case of parents who are not of sound mind, one is obligated to do all that is possible for them as long as they are living. The Code of Jewish Law also clarifies for us the definition of *honor,* which includes providing parents with food and drink, clothing, and assisting them in getting around.

The classic halachic work, *Chayei Adam* (67:12), written by Rabbi Avraham Danzig, remarks that the sustenance for one's parents is drawn from their income if they have the wherewithal. This would indicate that even though the parents have the means to pay for their food, there are other extenuating circumstances—particularly when it comes to the elderly. This would also include situations as discussed above, where the aging population experiences diminished appetite and feelings of despair and depression, stemming from the loss of a spouse, loneliness, or social isolation, and are no longer motivated to eat.

Therefore, it becomes incumbent upon the children, as part of the *mitzvah* of *kibbud av v'eim* – honoring father and mother — to make certain that their parents' food intake remains stable, ensuring the continuation of their well-being.

Some suggestions that might be implemented to ease this situation could include:

- Monitoring the intake of patients who experience weight loss
- Evaluating medications or physical limitations/impairments which may be causing the patient to limit food intake and modifying the factors when possible
- Making food visually appealing
- Encouraging small frequent meals
- Ensuring financial support services if needed

THE WORLD OF EATING DISORDERS

WHAT IS DIABULIMIA?

King David states in *Tehillim (103:15)*, "As for man, his days are like grass." The *Medrash Shmuel* expounds on this equating the human body to the tree; medicine to the fertilizer; and the physician to the one who plows the earth.

Diabulimia refers to individuals with Type I diabetes who intentionally skip or reduce their insulin doses in order to lose weight.

Type I diabetes is most often identified in children and young adults, and presents many overwhelming issues for the victims, especially young women. This is an autoimmune disease, where the cells that produce insulin are attacked by the body's own immune system. This prevents the body from absorbing the glucose and either burning it for energy or storing it as fat. The body begins to starve, and unused glucose floats uncontrolled in the bloodstream.

For many teenagers, being thin is more important to them than life itself. One of the first telltale signs when a young woman develops Type I diabetes is a sudden and dramatic weight loss; conversely, with the insulin injections the patient not only regains her lost weight but often puts on additional weight. Insulin is then perceived as "fat shots," and the diabetic, now in control of her own insulin intake, acquires the know-how to manipulate her doses in order to shed these unwanted pounds. In fact, researchers have found that Type I diabetic girls are two to three times more likely to develop an eating disorder than their non-diabetic peers. The young women become adept at secrecy, and take just enough insulin to avoid developing diabetic ketoacidosis requiring hospitalization.

Regrettably, the emphasis on food and weight that is an integral component of the diabetes treatment reflects the eating disorder mind-set. Similar to all eating disorders, diabulimia becomes a way for individuals to regain control of their life.

Signs and symptoms inclulde:

- Rapid weight loss or gain
- Irregular eating patterns
- Discomfort eating in the presence of others
- Poor body image
- Frequent dieting
- Low self-esteem
- Doubtful blood glucose monitoring

WHAT IS CUTTING?

I gave serious thought whether to present the following information in Starving Souls. I realize that many people will be shocked and distressed to read this, but there are, unfortunately, a number of people I see each year who are self-mutilators. For this reason, as a mitzvah k'avid – in order to provide helpful information for the health and welfare of those in desperate need – I decided to include this topic. If the subject matter is troubling to you, you do not need to read about it; it is merely available for your reference.

Cutting is an act of self-injury, whereby a person intentionally harms himself with a sharp object in order to draw blood. People who cut themselves do not usually intend to cause permanent damage. Many individuals who exhibit this behavior are experiencing difficult challenges in their life. It becomes a way of releasing their negative emotions or distracting them from their emotional pain. People who cut themselves see this as a way to relieve their inner pain by transferring it to the outside.

In the *Kinos* (Lamentations) which we read on *Tisha B'Av*, the poet cries, "Tear out your hair now and cut it off; mutilate your face." The point of reference here is the destruction of the Holy Temple and the ensuing calamities and tragedies that befell the Jewish nation. The horror triggers an expression of the deepest form of heartbreak and catastrophe, characterized by cutting and self-mutilation.

A similar phrase is used when the Prophet Micha expresses the mourning of the various Jewish cities when they are conquered by the Assyrian army *(1:16)*. "Make yourself bald and pull out your hair for the children of your delight; make your baldness broad like an eagle's, for they have departed from you!" It was common for the manifestation of extreme grief and traumatic experiences to be marked by self-mutilation.

The urge to cut might be triggered by:

- Strong feelings that a person is unable to express, such as anger, hurt, shame, frustration, or alienation
- A feeling of not "fitting in" or not being understood
- A need to escape a feeling of emptiness because of a loss
- Depression, bipolar disorder, an eating disorder or compulsive behaviors
- Problems with substance abuse

Problems that arise from self-mutilation:

- The depth of the cut is misjudged and may require stitches or hospitalization
- Cuts could be come infected
- When cutting becomes compulsive behavior it can seem impossible to stop
- The urge to cut becomes difficult to resist and what began as an initial attempt to feel more in control ends up taking control of the person.

Getting help is often problematic. Self-mutilators say that the most difficult aspect of getting help is admitting that they have this problem and talking about it. However, when they finally take that step and are able to speak about it they experience a strong sense of relief.

Here are some steps to take if someone you know is self-mutilating:

- Tell someone.
- Ask for help — have someone assist you in finding a competent mental health professional who can begin to guide the patient to healthier coping mechanisms.
- Identify the situations or emotions that are triggering the cutting, as the behavior is without doubt a reaction to emotional tension and pain.
- Once the patient is getting the necessary help, commitment and hard work are necessary to sort through one's difficult feelings and to express the pain. This will start the healing process and facilitate the training in coping with life's stressors.

Please remember a person who has a problem, a challenge or an addiction — even cutting — is not weak or crazy. These are normal people who are experiencing great emotional pain and they need our help.

WHAT IS PREGOREXIA?

The *Medrash* in *Shemos Rabbah* relates that when Moshe was leading the Jewish people out of Egypt, Hashem said to him, "How many babies are there? How many pregnant women are there? Have you prepared their food?"

The Eitz Yosef notes that this was a chaotic time, a time of transition, as the Jews were preparing for a journey into the wilderness, yet Hashem wanted to ensure the well-being of the pregnant women and the small infants.

How clearly this speaks for all generations, at all times, concerning the directive for pregnant women themselves to be mindful of their own health and welfare.

Pregorexia, the new buzzword referring to the condition of severe dieting and exercise during pregnancy, is actually nothing new. It is, however, a dangerous situation affecting pregnant women all over the world. Similar to the media ballyhoo of skinny personalities and icons, which impels teenagers to become anorexic, images of slim before-and-after pregnant celebrity moms are negatively impacting the average pregnancy in societies worldwide.

Obsessed with remaining thin, pregnant women are routinely exercising to the point of exhaustion while taking in far fewer calories than the body requires, putting their own health as well as the baby's health at risk .

Often, similar to the anorexic's experience, the patient is overwhelmed with feelings of shame and guilt, in this instance vis-à-vis her responsibility to the unborn child.

Mothers of average weight are usually advised to gain 25-35 pounds during pregnancy – i.e., towards the lower end of the range if they are overweight and more if they are underweight. Most physicians recommend a moderate amount of exercise, however it is not intended to control weight.

Risks of anorexia for the mom-to-be include:

- Calcium deficiencies, including loss of teeth and flaky fingernails
- Hypertension
- Depression
- Chronic pain
- Fatigue
- Insomnia

Risks of the mother's anorexia for the newborn include:

- Miscarriage or premature birth
- Low birth weight
- Neurological defects
- Cognitive, sensory and/or physical defects
- Respiratory problems
- Growth retardation
- Developmental disabilities

WHAT IS CYBEREXIA?

It is commonly known that the Internet has a dark side, preying on vulnerable adolescents and grown-ups to lure them into financial scams, abusive situations, or immoral or unethical behavior. However, more recently, adolescents and teenagers surfing the Web for *help* or information about eating disorders have instead become ensnared in the tentacles of "pro-ana" (pro-anorexia) and "pro-mia" (pro-bulimia) sites.

These websites, in effect, promote eating disorders as a lifestyle choice rather than an illness. The surreality of transforming a serious life-threatening disease into friends, i.e. "Ana" and "Mia," with whom one would like to spend time, is frightening. With the click of a mouse, impressionable young people meet peers who offer their personal "success" stories about losing weight, tips for easier purging and dieting techniques, and when to exercise. Group members support each other by fasting together in solidarity, commiserating with one another after breaking a fast, and offering suggestions on how to conceal their behaviors from parents and doctors. Inspiration and encouragement to achieve the "perfect" body are presented with pictures of waif-thin models and movie stars as well as appealing quotes such as, "Nothing tastes as good as thin feels."

The proliferation of social networking sites that advocate for anorexics and bulimics is alarming, as they only serve to deter recovery in eating disordered patients.

When Hashem destroyed the city of Sodom and all its inhabitants, Lot and his family were saved. However, we read (*Bereishis 19:26*) that Lot's wife took a quick glance behind her and turned into a pillar of salt. What egregious sin did Lot's wife commit by peeking to see what they had left behind?

Our Sages explain that Lot's wife was, so to speak, "in recovery." She had been extricated from Sodom, the core of depravity, and was standing at an important crossroads in her life. She now had the opportunity to elevate herself to a new spiritual and moral level. Yet Lot's wife chose to give a backward glance at what she was leaving behind. A momentary glimpse backwards or revisiting detrimental forces and influences in our life has the power to make us lose our footing and fail to make forward progress.

Interestingly, experimental studies in the last few years among girls and young women found that those who participated in a single viewing of pro-ana websites were more likely to have lower self-esteem and become preoccupied with exercise and weight loss.

Oftentimes, therapists working with eating-disordered patients are unaware of their faceless, yet strong, competition – namely, cyberspace – and are puzzled by the patient's lack of progress.

Once therapists are cognizant of the anorexic's devotion to the pro-ana sites, they should:

- Assess the general frequency and amount of Internet usage by the patient
- Address underlying issues that attract the patient to these websites, i.e., communication, identification with others
- Redirect the patient to resources that offer positive input to counter the effect of the pro-ana/mia sites
- In no way directly forbid the patient from accessing these sites, but offer more constructive or beneficial websites for perusal.

Signs of Internet addiction include:

- A need for increasing amounts of time on the Internet to achieve satisfaction
- Using the Internet to escape problems or relieve feelings of helplessness or depression
- Development of withdrawal symptoms upon cutback or termination of Internet usage, i.e. obsessive thinking about what is happening on the Internet

- Failed attempts to control Internet access
- Withdrawal from other pleasurable activities
- Reduction or loss of social or career relationships

It is interesting to note that the word for "friend" in Hebrew is *chaver*. Its letters – *ches, vais, reish* – when rearranged spell *cherev*, which is the Hebrew word for sword. This would suggest that friends can be reliable and trustworthy or lethal as a sword. The word *chaver* can also be reordered to form the root word of "to flee – *bais, reish, ches*"; so if we find ourself in a destructive relationship, we should flee.

When a person surfs the Internet, "meeting" people and forming friendships, it would be wise to contemplate whether he has indeed met "a *chaver*", a friend, or a *"cherev,"* a dangerous companion from whom he should flee in haste.

SPIRITUAL CONFLICTS

BECKY'S STORY

One usually associates South Africa with lions, elephants, jungles and swamps. To be quite frank, up until recently, those were the first images that came to my mind. However, after a week's lecture tour through South Africa, I now think immediately of a thriving, inspired and enthusiastic Jewish community, that left an indelible impression on me.

It was a cool summer evening. I was to give a lecture on the theme of truth, in a very large auditorium in the center of Johannesburg. A huge crowd of people had turned out for the lecture, and additional seating had to be quickly arranged. There was literally not an inch of space that wasn't filled.

At the end of the hour-and-a-half talk, there was an opportunity for the members of the audience to ask questions and have a private consultation. I don't remember all the questions that were asked. They were the usual – a halachic inquiry about Shabbos, a question on the topic of truth, a question on the Torah perspective of a relationship …

There was, however, one question that totally shook me to the core.

A young woman hesitantly approached me. She appeared to be unsure whether or not to ask her question. Finally, she lowered her eyes and asked if I thought her parents would forgive her if she died.

I was shocked. Many questions ran through my mind at that moment. Why was this young girl, who appeared to have her whole life in front of her, contemplating her own death? What morbid reality was she facing? Was she contemplating suicide? Was she on drugs? No child thinks of her own mortality unless confronted by a situation that makes life seem precarious and fragile.

Fortunately, Hashem gave me the right words to draw out her pain. I asked her if she thought her parents loved her.

With great conviction she answered, "Yes, very much so," nodding her head emphatically.

"Parents who love, forgive their children for many things, so whatever it is that is troubling you, remember that. Now tell me, why did you ask such a question?"

She explained to me that she was suffering from an eating disorder. Her physical health – her heart, kidneys and other vital functions – had deteriorated to the point that her doctors had warned her that her life could come to an abrupt end. She described, in horrifying detail, her downward physical spiral and how slowly but surely her life was ebbing away. She then repeated her question: "Do you think my parents would ever forgive me if I died?"

I thought for a moment and then answered: "Knowing that your parents love you so deeply, it could be that they will come to a level of forgiveness. However, what I am not sure of is if your children will be able to forgive you."

The young woman, who up to this point had been lethargic and withdrawn, displayed keen interest. "What do you mean – my children? I'm not even married yet!"

I gently explained to her that we have been given the sacred mission to bring children into this world. It is brought down in the mystical books, that under the *chuppah* the couple is joined by the children destined to be born from the ensuing marriage. Hashem wants those children to be born. "I am not sure that the children that you were destined to give birth to will be able to understand why they were not given their chance to live."

At that point, the young lady broke down and cried.

We discussed her situation for quite some time, and by the time we concluded our meeting she had agreed to enter a new program that could help her gain a new perspective on life.

That evening was a turning point in her life. The last I heard she was doing better and putting great effort into restoring her health.

This story, through the great beneficence of Hashem, ended happily. We must realize, however, how many thousands are consumed and ultimately overwhelmed by this challenge, forfeiting their very lives.

Overview

People have spiritual conflicts. You don't get an eating disorder because you have spiritual conflicts; you get spiritual conflicts when you have an eating disorder because you just feel horrible. I hated Shabbos. I hated Yom Tov. Shabbos, to be truthful, was the hardest time. I was in the bathroom fifty times. With Yom Tov — forget it.

— Miriam, a 20-year-old anorexic patient

There are many factors that must be considered when trying to understand eating disorders. There are psychological factors, cultural factors, biological factors, and religious factors. One of the greatest dilemmas that a person suffering from an eating disorder can be faced with occurs when the illness begins to interfere with a deep-rooted religious observance or tradition. Then the patient becomes strongly torn between two conflicting spheres of persuasion.

On the one hand, the powerful influence of an eating disorder has been likened, by many, to a real friend. Many patients have coined a name to refer to their eating disorder. For example, one anorexic who came to see me referred to his eating disorder as "Anna." In the context of our conversation, it became difficult at times to remember that he was talking about the eating disorder and not about a real person.

Contrast this with the deeply-rooted Torah commitment that has been inculcated in the individual in utero, when the Angel taught the child the entire Torah. This innate nurturing fosters an irrepressible need to conform and be part of the community.

In fact, the patient is often more plagued by this conflict than by the initial underlying cause of the eating disorder itself. She becomes distressed with feelings of guilt and self-reproach, as she is forced to choose between her religious observance and her need to support her eating disorder.

For example, before every fast day, especially before *Yom Kippur* and *Tisha B'Av*, I receive numerous calls concerning whether to fast or abstain from fasting. After gathering all the pertinent facts, obtaining the doctor's opinion and data, and assessing the patient's condition, a decision is reached. Invariably, the decision is questioned. If the patient is told not to fast, he will not find comfort in that decision and will try to counter with reasons why he should fast. The argument often goes like this, "But why shouldn't I fast? I fast every day anyhow. It won't be different than any 'regular' day." Many will call a second time, right before the fast, just to double-check that they shouldn't fast.

When I realized the great difficulties that people with eating disorders were experiencing when faced with a fast day, I composed a special prayer to be recited by those who had been instructed to eat on a fast day.[1]

I receive numerous referrals from doctors who feel that a patient needs religious counseling, in addition to medical and therapeutic interventions. This is only one example of the many spiritual conflicts that occur in the course of daily living of a patient with an eating disorder. In order to facilitate the therapy and recovery of an eating disorder patient, consideration of the spiritual factor is significant.

---

[1] See the chapter titled: Prayers Related to Recovery

Our objective here is to provide general insight into some of the religious issues and challenges faced by observant patients. This will, in turn, afford a more comprehensive understanding all of the components that need to be addressed to effectively heal the patient.

LIFE

You shall observe My decrees and My laws... by which man will live

-Vayikra 18:5

The *Gemara (Sanhedrin 74a)* adds, "You should live by them and not die by them."

The Chofetz Chaim calls attention here to a basic tenet of our Jewish belief. Our Sages tell us that the 248 positive *mitzvos* in the Torah represent the 248 limbs of man. Every single *mitzvah* gives life to one of the limbs.

We all understand that it is feasible for a human being to survive and function in this world without one or more of some limbs, such as a hand or a foot. He would be considered a *baal mum* – disabled. However, there are other parts of the body that are vital for the human being's existence. If they are damaged or impaired, the human being cannot continue to survive.

So, too, explains the Chofetz Chaim, the *mitzvos* represent the sustenance of our life. One can transgress certain *mitzvos* and only be a *baal mum* – impaired. However, there are other *mitzvos* that are the main life-giving source of our *neshamos*. If one does not observe these *mitzvos* he is endangering the well-being and possibly the very existence of his soul.

The Vilna Gaon elaborates, in a similar vein, on the *pasuk* in *Mishlei (13:13)*, "He who scorns a word will cause himself injury, but he who reveres a commandment will be rewarded." He who scorns one of the *mitzvos* in the Torah, shows contempt for himself, because he is lacking the revitalizing essence of that *mitzvah*. But one who reveres the Torah's commandments *"yeshulam"* [from the root word *shalem*, complete], his limbs will be whole.

Therefore the Torah commands us to observe all the *mitzvos* of Hashem, *"v'chai bahem* – so that man will live."

In fact, every commandment in the Torah is a source of life and well-being for the individual. All the *mitzvos* are in consonance with a person's physical health and mental well-being. Therefore, for example, if it is not possible for a person to fast on *Yom Kippur* – to the extent that it would be life-threatening – he must eat. If the doctor orders the patient to take non-kosher medicine that is crucial to his health, there is no question that he must ingest this remedy

The Chazon Ish, Rabbi Avraham Yeshaya Karelitz (1878-1953) notes that human effort in matters pertaining to health is a *mitzvah* and an obligation upon every person. It is considered one of the Torah dictums necessary to attain a higher level of perfection. The more a person takes care of himself, the higher the level of spirituality he reaches.

The Zohar says that through our fulfillment of the *mitzvos* we elevate the entire creation to the point where it becomes clearly evident that the Torah is the mainstay of the world's very existence.

So important is maintaining one's health that the Talmud tells us (*Sanhedrin 17b*) that it is prohibited for a Torah scholar to dwell in a city that does not have a doctor.

Oftentimes, people are drawn to a certain city by the advertisements that publicize the location's amenities, such as kosher eateries, synagogues within walking distance, schools, and so on. Yet, our Sages tell us that it is important to ascertain what kind of medical care is available in the area before making a decision to move to that city.

The reason the Talmud invokes this prohibition specifically for the *talmid chacham* (Torah scholar) and not the common man is probably based on the principle that since we rely on our Torah scholars to guide the way, it is understood that if the Torah scholar would not live in a specific location, then a common person would follow his example and not choose to live there, either.

FULFILLMENT

You will eat and you will be satisfied, and bless Hashem for the good land that He gave you.
-The *mitzvah* of *Birchas HaMazon* (Grace After Meals),
Mitzvah 430[2]

The Zohar explains that the *mitzvah* does not imply that one has to fill his stomach in order to bless Hashem. A person may eat only a *kezayis* (lit., the size of an olive) of bread, and if his intention is to make this the core of his nourishment it is also considered satisfaction and the person must recite the *Birchas HaMazon*.

Technically speaking, a person only has to recite the Grace After Meals when he eats a *kezayis* of bread. If a person eats less than this required amount, he is not obligated to say the *Birchas HaMazon*.

The Chazon Ish was one of the greatest Torah luminaries of recent times. His views, actions, halachic rulings and writings continue to have a major influence on the fabric of Torah life everywhere. In his judgment, the amount of a *kezayis* is the cubic volume of slightly less than 1 fluid ounce, or .96 of a fluid ounce. The following measurements constitute a *kezayis* of the specific bread:

---

[2] *Devarim, 8:10*

1/10 of a bagel (13 grams)
1/9 of a challah roll (5 grams)
1/3 of a slice of white bread (8 grams)
1/4 of a pita bread (12 grams)[3]

A question that arises is this: What if a person eats the required *kezayis* of bread, but then purges in the middle of the meal, before saying *Birchas HaMazon*? Is the *Birchas HaMazon* still obligatory, because in truth a *kezayis* of bread was ingested? Or is the individual no longer required to recite the *Birchas HaMazon* because that *kezayis* of bread is no longer in his digestive tract?

The Ketzos HaChoshen rules that one must determine to what degree the person has regurgitated. If all the food that has been eaten has been regurgitated, and not even a *kezayis* of food has remained with him, then he would not be able to recite the *Birchas HaMazon*. If it is possible to ascertain that a *kezayis* still remains within him, then he would be able to recite the *Birchas HaMazon*.

It should be noted that many bulimics will wait for an opportune time during the course of the meal itself to purge. One of the reasons for this conduct is that the individual begins to experience a trapped feeling. Seated around a table, laden with abundant food, and surrounded by family and others who are focused on eating, the bulimic begins to internalize all the consumption of food taking place to the point where she feels "stuffed" and has an extreme need to purge. In addition, everyone around the table is involved in conversation and eating the meal, so the purger can disappear from the table without attracting much attention.

In general, "satisfaction" is difficult to assess when dealing with eating disordered patients. That is because the individual never really achieves the state of "satisfaction." The anorexic eats because she knows that she must eat, but is actually "dissatisfied" with the food that she has consumed. The

---

[3] *Sefer Kezayis HaShalem*

bulimic, on the other hand, never achieves the status of "satisfaction" because he is feeding an emotional hunger that is insatiable.

"Individuals with anorexia don't lose their appetite. They are hungry all the time, although they lose hunger awareness once malnutrition sets in."[4]

The guilt, fear, anxiety and obsessive thoughts involved in eating does not allow the eating disorder patient to ever realize a true sense of satisfaction.

"Emotional eating is the domain of the compulsive eater, chronic dieter, bulimic and anorexic. Although each uses food in a different way – gorging, bingeing, and purging, or starving – all are using food as a drug that can soothe, comfort, and keep them company or even punish and hurt them for their guilty feelings."[5]

In the context of eating on Shabbos or *Yom Tov* for *oneg Shabbos* – taking pleasure in Shabbos, or *oneg Yom Tov,* the anorexic patient is consumed with the guilt of not eating the meal that is part of the observance of the day. An anorexic patient asked me, "What if my *oneg Shabbos* is actually not to eat?"

This is actually a very interesting question. A parallel can be drawn with one who has a disturbing dream on Friday night, and the Sages rule that fasting is the proper antidote. The question then arises: Should we fast on Shabbos or not? The Chofetz Chaim states that although under normal circumstances it would disrupt the enjoyment of the day, in this case the fasting will give the person who has had a bad dream peace of mind with the knowledge that the fast has the power to "neutralize" a disturbing dream.[6]

---

[4] Dr. Ira M. Sacker, *Regaining Your Self*
[5] Mary Anne Cohen, *French Toast for Breakfast*
[6] *Mishnah Berurah, 288:15*

HONOR AND RESPECT

Honor your father and your mother, so that your days will be lengthened ...

-Mitzvah 33[7]

Rav Abba, the son of Kahana, said: In the Torah the very easiest of the commandments is equated with the most difficult. The easiest commandment is that of sending away the mother bird; the most difficult is that of honoring father and mother. And regarding both of them it is written, "And you will extend your years."

The Chayei Adam quotes our Sages who tell us that all the obligations that a child has to fulfill for his parents are in payment for all the good that they have bestowed upon him.

The commandment to honor one's father and mother is a foundation of Judaism. It is one of the *Aseres HaDibros,* the Ten Commandments, and its guidelines are extensive. Included in this commandment is the injunction not to contradict a parent .[8]

This exhortation for children to exhibit the proper respect for their parents creates an untenable situation of conflict for the eating disorder patient. Children raised in observant homes are introduced to the *mitzvah* of *kibbud av v'eim* (honoring father and mother) from a very early age. Already in preschool, children are responsible for weekend assignments, such as "being respectful to parents" or "not waking the parent on Shabbos afternoon."

---

[7] *Shemos, 20:12*
[8] *Code of Jewish Laws, 240:2*

Therefore, when the anorexic is challenged by the parent or must be oppositional, the patient's moral dilemma is further heightened and the situation becomes even more stressful.

The parent will say to the child, "Please eat, you're losing too much weight." The child will respond, "That's not true. I'm not losing weight."

The parent will plead with the child to seek proper medical and psychological attention, and the child will refuse. "I don't need help; I don't want to see anybody."

Annoyed, the parent yells, "If you truly wanted to get better, you would stop this." The child, equally frustrated, shouts back, "I cannot do that."

Another component of the commandment of *kibbud av v'eim* involves not causing distress to the parent. The Zohar teaches us[9] that the Matriarch Rachel did not merit to raise her son Binyamin because she stole the idols from her father Lavan, greatly paining him. Although Rachel's intentions were completely pure, she exhibited a lack of sensitivity in her actions, and for that she was punished with this fate.

Many of the behaviors of patients with eating disorders seem to be directed against their parents. Often the bulimic will deliberately leave evidence of her activity so a parent will discover it. This conduct may be motivated by anger and/or bitterness, and a wish to offend the parent.

It is ironic to note that often a factor in the initial onset of an eating disorder is an unsatisfactory parent-child relationship. Even though there is a strong parental investment of time and energy in raising children, parents may have unrealistic expectations of their children or may make unfair psychological projections that ultimately have a negative impact on a child's healthy body image and self-esteem.

---

[9] *Zohar, Volume 1, 164*

Nevertheless, the patient will often ultimately comment to me, "What I wanted most was my parents' attention. Once I got it, I could no longer accept it."

An anorexic patient who was consulting me was troubled because he had been disrespectful to his parents and he wanted to ask *mechilah* – forgiveness. His dilemma focused on the halachic ramifications involved if he repeated his disrespectful behavior. He stated that until the onset of his illness he had been extremely deferential to his parents. He had never been oppositional or in any way caused his parents distress.

I discussed with him various aspects of the concept of *teshuvah* (repentance). I explained that it is important for a person to repent for his transgression at the first opportunity, in hopes that the repentance will be long-lasting and the transgression will not be repeated. I also stressed the importance of repenting for each wrongdoing on its own, rather than allowing an accumulation of lapses.

One more consideration that must be included in the context of this topic would be some insight from the parents' perspective, who sometimes become an easy target when looking to place blame for problems that crop up in a family. Often the parents of a child with an eating disorder are beleaguered with feelings of guilt. They feel that the disorder reflects poorly on their parenting skills or is a direct result of a dysfunctional family unit.

This could not be further from the truth. Although it is possible that a dysfunctional family unit can greatly contribute to the development of a child with an eating disorder, it is not the exclusive cause of this occurrence. "Parents are primarily responsible for defining the world in which their children find themselves, but the emergence of an eating disorder is not in itself a response to a specific social structure within the family."[10]

The nightmarish life of parents of a child with an eating disorder tests their strength, patience and wisdom and pushes them to the limit. It is an ex-

---

[10] Peggy Claude-Pierre, *The Secret Language of Eating Disorders*

perience that one can only pray to survive intact. Nevertheless, the vast majority of parents are willing to selflessly sacrifice themselves to ensure their child's treatment and recovery.

A parent in our local community literally took a leave of absence from his job in order to dedicate himself to taking care of all the necessary arrangements - transportation, doctors' visits, and hospital visits to ensure his daughter's well-being.

SEPARATION ANXIETY

Do not separate yourself from the community[11]

The Rambam[12] explains that when those who were righteous feared that they themselves might become influenced by association with people who are evil, they would flee the community and society. They wanted to protect their morals and ideals from becoming corrupt by terminating any possible interaction between them.

The Tiferes Yisroel comments in this context that one should not disengage from the *minhagim,* customs, of the *tzibbur* (society). The Talmud tells us[13] that when Moshe Rabbeinu went up to Heaven he didn't eat, since the Heavenly angels did not partake of food. Conversely, when the angels came down to earth to see Avraham, they ate the bread that he offered them.

One of the predominant principles in Judaism is the concept of community. Many activities center around school, synagogue, organizations, and the like. The community serves as a valuable support system and is integral to

---

[11] *Pirkei Avos, 1:5*
[12] *Shemone Perakim, Chapter 4*
[13] *Bava Metzia 86b*

the observance of Judaism and its *mitzvos*. It allows for important inter-facing, sharing of ideas and is usually a source of strength and comfort.

As such, there is an innate desire for every person to be accepted as part of the group/community and to be approved of by others. A person who is ex-periencing challenges with an eating disorder, though, may find himself slowly disassociating from the community. He no longer seems to share the same goals as the others. Relative to his personal situation, his needs, and his emotional upheaval, he feels disoriented and no longer on the same wavelength as his peers. Although he craves the regular social interaction, he feels detached from others and not worthy of having "normal" friends. "Some sufferers feel that they have a guilty secret they carry around with them, where they are able to eat 'normally' in public, only for this control to break down when alone. Many feel very isolated."[14] The eating disor-der patient tends to disengage further, as he begins to feel that others can-not relate to his experiences.

In addition, the eating disorder patient realizes that people may be talking about her, her illness may have become public knowledge, someone is aware that she is seeking professional help, or her problem is apparent from her ap-pearance, and she is ashamed and wishes to spare herself the embarrassment of discomfiting stares or questions.

A young woman in an insular community in England told me in a phone conversation that after she had read my book, *Starving to Live,* she was greatly comforted because until then she had been unaware that there were others like herself, from a similar religious background, who had eating dis-orders.

However, once an individual has made the choice not to belong, or not to participate in community life, it reinforces strong feelings of being an out-sider, a non-conformist, a loner.

---

[14] Anna Paterson, *Beating Eating Disorders*

A young man had been attending a weekly Torah class that I was giving. After not seeing him for a number of weeks, I called to inquire about his health. He explained that although he actually enjoyed coming to class, it was easier for him to stay at home and listen over the phone to the class. In that way he could avoid answering uncomfortable questions concerning his weight.

The Talmud, in *Taanis 23a,* tells of Choni HaMa'agal, Choni "the Circle-Maker," a great rabbinic scholar, who slept miraculously for seventy years. When he awoke, he went to see his family. However, a generation had passed, and the family he knew were no longer alive. The grandchildren did not believe that he was their grandfather as, the commentaries explain, it was assumed that he had been killed in war. He went to the *bais medrash,* and there, too, they did not believe that he was Choni HaMa'agal. Choni was completely distraught about his lack of companionship and begged Hashem to have mercy upon him. If Choni, such an exalted personage, experienced such desperation, it is difficult to imagine the depths of despair and pain felt by those who have become isolated from the rest of the community as a result of their eating disorder.

HEALTH WATCH

Take great heed with your souls[15]

We receive guidance from the Torah that all matters pertaining to human life and health should be carefully regarded. The Rambam states[16] that refraining from at-risk activity is derived from the *pasuk,* "*Hishamer lecha u'shmor nafshecha me'od* — Guard yourself and guard your soul".[17]

---

[15] *Devarim, 4:15*
[16] *Hilchos Rotzei'ach, 11:4*
[17] *Devarim, 4:9*

The great rabbis of the Talmud recorded in detail specific remedies and potions, as well as foods and herbs with medicinal qualities, that were found to be beneficial to one's health. The Rambam in *Hilchos Dei'os* writes extensively concerning healthful eating and drinking practices, proper hygiene, proper physical exertion and sleeping routines that are healthful. Books have been published with comprehensive guidelines on *shemiras haguf* – how to keep ourselves healthy.

There is also the rabbinic injunction against *chovel atzmo* – injuring oneself without a valid reason. In this context, people who put themselves in harm's way, that is, put themselves in physical or mortal danger, are culpable for their oversight.

The renowned Rabbi Moshe Feinstein (1895-1986), one of the foremost halachic authorities of our generation, addresses the issue of one who inflicts pain on himself by dieting, that is, "crash dieting." Although the dieter does not intend to inflict pain, it is a natural consequence of abstaining from food. He writes:

> "… when a person diets to the extent that he/she actually experiences hunger pangs, although such hunger will not cause one to fall ill, such dieting is likened to self-inflicted destruction. It is not permitted even for purposes of monetary gain or other pleasure."[18]

Many patients also go through the phase of denial. The premise of the anorexic is that even though she hasn't eaten for "x" number of days, she is "still around." Similarly, the bulimic insists that she has been purging for more than a year and she's "still here." Their mortality somehow does not come into question, and their perception is that they will continue to live. Yet people with eating disorders have the highest mortality rate of those with any mental illness. [19]

---

[18] *Igros Moshe Choshen Mishpat 65*
[19] *South Carolina Department of Mental Health*

For many in the throes of an eating disorder, it is very difficult to perceive the injurious effects of their behavior on their personal health. However, when it is brought to their attention, they are conflicted. They are aware of the Torah admonition to guard one's health, but yet they are powerless in attempting to adhere to that dictum.

Incredible as this may sound, it is even more difficult when the patient has crossed over to "cutting." Although the anorexic or bulimic patient may not have visible signs of damage to his health, the "cutter" actually has the evidence of the damage right in front of him. He sees the blood flowing from the wound, the marks of his cuts, the scars on his skin. The self-mutilator, though, is not someone who can articulate his feelings clearly. Many cutters are awkward in explaining their thoughts about themselves and their relationships with others.

Yet the rationale is the same with all of them. The patient with an eating disorder has an uncontrollable compulsion to express his need through his body. For some, expression is found through regurgitation; for others it is through the withholding of food; and sometimes he expresses his need with his own flesh.

One cutter once told me that when she cuts herself she feels she is alive. The self-mutilator, enmeshed in mental disintegration and a loss of perspective, contemplates how much pain he can take, how much disfigurement of his skin he can tolerate, how much bleeding he can withstand.[20]

A 27-year-old graduate student related that she had an eating disorder in high school along with depression. "I then began to self-mutilate," she continued, "because I was always taught by those close to me to keep my feelings inside."

What is most important to understand is that in these circumstances willpower is not enough! "Don't you see that you are killing yourself?" be-

---

[20] Steven Levenkron, *Cutting*

comes a rhetorical question, because the eating disorder patient cannot do anything about it.

Let me relate to you a conversation I had with a patient in California. After reviewing the patient's most recent blood tests, the doctor rendered a very grim prognosis. The patient was upset, and asked me for words of encouragement. In attempting to offer the patient hope, I remarked with much optimism that we would just have to devise a new way of rescuing him from the clutches of this illness.

The patient looked at me quizzically and said, "If you think that perhaps I want to die, the answer is no. However, if you are suggesting that I must take leave of this disorder in order to live, the answer is I cannot let go."

TRUTH

Distance yourself from a false word[21]

The great Rav Simcha Bunim of Psischa comments that no other transgression in the Torah is stated with the warning to distance oneself from it. The severity of telling a lie is great, and Hashem detests falsehood to the extent that we are commanded to remain distant from it. In fact, the signature of Hashem is *emes* – truth.

So important is the exhortation to be truthful, that each morning in our prayers we ask, "Always let a person be God-fearing privately, and acknowledge the truth and speak the truth within his heart." Not only should a person publicly admit to the truth, but he should even speak truth in his heart.

---

[21] *Shemos, 23:7*

This presents an unusually difficult dilemma for the person who has rarely told an untruth in the past. The person with an eating disorder finds it necessary to lie in order to protect himself and to avoid punishment. Avoiding conflict through people-pleasing or other methods does not resolve the problem. If patients will not acknowledge or engage in any conflict, their issues and problems have very little chance of getting solved.[22] With the passage of time and their success at deceiving others, the lying gets worse and they are impelled to continue the deception. Patients with eating disorders feel that their survival depends on their ability to avoid saying the truth at all costs. Most of their daily conduct is predicated on some form of untruth – whether it is a modification of the truth, an alteration of the truth, or an outright falsehood.

Individuals with an eating disorder are extremely secretive and determined to conceal their disease. They remain on guard to keep their purging or fasting unknown to others. It therefore becomes very difficult, often, for the bystander to identify the presence of the eating disorder.

This has prompted researchers, in the last few years, to develop a new test that is able to analyze a few strands of hair to determine whether someone is actually anorexic or bulimic. It has been found that as our hair grows, new proteins attach to the base of each strand. These proteins, which are produced and influenced by whatever we eat, push the strand up and out of the individual hair follicle. The hair, in effect, records a person's nutritional health. Two of the proteins under analysis —carbon and nitrogen – enable researchers to detect eating disorders. Similar to drug addicts who have to submit to routine drug-testing to determine whether they are being rehabilitated, individuals suspected of suffering from an eating disorder can be identified by scientific analysis.

Anorexics and bulimics will sometimes wear a weighted belt underneath their clothing for weigh-ins in order to belie their loss of weight. In an attempt to avoid shame or embarrassment individuals with eating disorders

---

[22] Dr. Harriet Braiker, *The Disease to Please*

become adept at disguising their behaviors. When they are confronted, they may lie multiple times in response to the barrage of questions that they cannot answer truthfully, such as, "Did you eat lunch? Did you eat everything I gave you? Did you purge today?"

The following halachic question was posed to Rabbeinu Chaim Berlin: Is it permissible to ask someone a question that he will most likely answer untruthfully, since it might involve the negative prohibition of *"Lifnei iver lo siten michshol* – Do not place a stumbling block before a blind person,"* that is, cause another person to sin.[23] Rabbeinu Berlin answered that if the questioner knows that his friend will respond untruthfully to his line of questioning, he theeby indeed becomes the means of causing the other person to sin.[24]

A young man with an eating disorder was made to eat every meal under the watchful eye of his parent in order to monitor his intake of food. However, the young man contrived to evade scrutiny by having a pocket sewn inside his sweater near his neck. Unobserved, he would take the food off the plate, pretend he was putting it into his mouth, and then surreptitiously drop it into the pocket and hide it there. His strategy remained undetected for many months.

Yet the feelings of guilt, shame, remorse and self-reproach that are evoked within the patient with the eating disorder are equally painful and distressing to him. It is an inner struggle that the individual confronts on a daily basis, even as he continues this behavior.

Although it may be very painful to disclose an eating disorder to a parent, one should not hide the fact from a parent. Even if the patient feels that an underlying cause of her eating disorder may be a parent, the family unit will ultimately need to be involved, in any case. In order to facilitate the patient's healing and recovery, all causal issues will need to be brought to light and resolved.

---

[23] *Vayikra, 19:14*
[24] *Nishmas Chaim, 192*

A graduate student once confided that the young man she was seeing kept asking her why she rarely agreed to go out with him to eat. She had offered many explanations, such as preferring not to focus so much on food, and not liking to eat in front of so many people. When they did go out to eat, she would barely pick at the food in her plate and he would ask, "Is the food to your liking? Are you feeling okay? Do you want to order something else on the menu?"

"Truthfully," said the young woman, "I am simply lying." And then she added, "I feel like my whole life is a lie."

I told her that her whole life was not a lie. Perhaps it was only a lie in this specific area.

Her response was, "This specific area **IS** my whole life right now."

DAY OF REST

Six days shall you do your activities and on the seventh day you shall rest

Mitzvah 85[25]

One of the basic tenets of the Jewish faith is observance of the Shabbos. By observing the Shabbos and not doing any work, the Jew testifies that Hashem is the master of the world. Moreover, we are commanded to rest *(menucha)*. Our Sages explain that this implies much more than physical rest. It is an attitude of mind, a spiritual state, induced by the experience that is Shabbos. Dayan Grunfeld states in his *sefer*[26], "The spirit of *menucha* finds its positive expression in the Sabbath meals in which the happy companionship of family and friends, the enjoyment of food,

---

[25] *Shemos, 20:6*
[26] *The Sabbath*

the table-songs in praise of Hashem and the Sabbath, all combine to form an entire unique experience."

The *pasuk* states[27] "If you proclaim the Sabbath 'a delight' … and you honor it … then you will delight in Hashem." It is explained, in fact, that the observance of Shabbos is manifest with both our physical and spiritual being. When we give honor to the Shabbos and derive corporal enjoyment from it, we are able to grasp a higher level of spiritual delight, because even the material aspects of the day have become imbued with spirituality.

The simple *mitzvah* of partaking in the three Sabbath meals, which is incumbent upon men and women alike,[28] is one that presents an unbelievable challenge for the patient with an eating disorder.

Many individuals with an eating disorder have an obsessive need to keep track of their weight at all times. Others become addicted to compulsive, excessive exercise. Both of these activities present difficult challenges for one who is observant. Weighing oneself is included among the prohibitions of Shabbos.[29]

The act of weighing oneself is classified as an *uvda d'chol* – a weekday activity one must refrain from doing on Shabbos.

The scale itself is considered to be *muktzah,* set apart from being used on Shabbos, because it falls in the category of *keilim shemelachtam l'issur.* This category relates to utensils whose primary function is one that is prohibited on Shabbos, such as weighing oneself.

Although engaging in intense exercise may be a source of pure enjoyment for some, and may technically be permissible according to basic halacha, it would nevertheless be in the category of *uvda d'chol* (weekday activity) and is therefore also disallowed.

---

[27] *Yeshayah, 58:13*
[28] *Code of Jewish Law, 291:6*
[29] *Code of Jewish Laws, 323, Par. 1*

The classification of *uvda d'chol* is understood to include any activity that looks like work or would eventually be followed by work or labor. Our rabbis also include in this category any activity that is not in consonance with the holiness and sanctity of the Sabbath day.

This is derived from the Talmud,[30] which states, "The way that you walk on Shabbos should not be the way you walk on a weekday," that is, in accord with the spirit and majesty of the Shabbos. As a result, one should not rush or hurry, nor pursue athletic sports.

The individual with an eating disorder sometimes has a need to act out his emotional tension by practicing self-injurious behavior. The act of self-mutilation encompasses many Torah sanctions, but on Shabbos there is the additional prohibition of causing oneself to bleed.[31]

The Talmud discusses the phenomenon of inducing vomiting in public,[32] and Rashi explains that that practice was extant among those who either wished to actually empty their stomach in order to eat more, or to relieve pressure caused by overeating. There is further discussion in the Talmud[33] concerning inducing vomiting on Shabbos. Rabba bar bar Chana cites R' Yochanan that this is only prohibited when it is effected by a drug, but not when it is done by hand. Then again, such action could certainly not be deemed to be within the "spirit" of the Shabbos. R' Nechemiah states, however, there would even be a consideration this practice be prohibited during the week because of the waste of food.

Shabbos is often used as a measure of one's commitment to Judaism. The absence or diminution of this entire experience weighs heavily on the individual with an eating disorder. Surrounded by family, visitors and guests, the patient has less private time and any of his/her activities are more open to observation, discovery, and reprimand or ridicule.

---

[30] *Shabbos 113b*
[31] *Mishnah Berurah, 316, Par. 30*
[32] *Shabbos 12a*
[33] *Shabbos 147b*

Finally, aside from their disregard for this aspect of Shabbos/Yom Tov observance, patients are burdened with the knowledge that they are engaging in activities that are forbidden on Shabbos and are not participating in the pleasure of the Shabbos.

ATONEMENT

On the tenth day of this month it is Yom HaKippurim ... you shall afflict yourselves ... for it is a Day of Atonement to provide you atonement before Hashem.[34]

Mitzvos 313 and 316, concerning the fast day of *Yom HaKippurim*, are derived from this *pasuk*. Our Sages teach us that "affliction" is the Torah's designation for not eating and drinking. Fasting on *Yom Kippur* constitutes a *mitzvah d'oraysa*, a commandment of Biblical origin with stringent ramifications.

Our focus on *Yom Kippur* is directed toward achieving true repentance. Our Sages explain that abstention from food and drink and other physical pleasures frees us to concentrate solely on this effort. Fasting is an important element of repentance in and of itself.

In addition to *Yom Kippur*, which is cited in the Torah, the Talmud[35] discusses four other fast days that commemorate the destruction of *Bayis Rishon* and *Bayis Sheini* (the First and Second Temples) and the exile of the Jewish People from Eretz Yisroel – *Tzom Gedaliah, Asarah B'Teves, Shivah Asar B'Tammuz* and *Tisha B'Av*. In contrast to the first three, the *halachos* of *Tisha B'Av* are the strictest and comparable to the Fast of *Yom Kippur*.

---

[34] *Vayikra, 23:27*
[35] *Rosh Hashanah 18b*

Two additional, rabbinically ordained, fasts on the Jewish calendar are *Taanis Esther*[36] and *Taanis Bechorim*.[37]

This area of Jewish observance seems to present a unique dilemma for the observant eating disorder patient.

> *The Talmud*[38] *states that one who is ill should, upon the advice of experts, be fed. If there are no experts present he should be fed according to his own assessment, until he says he has had enough.*
>
> *Mar Rav Bar Ashi states that if one hundred experts agree that the ill person has no need to eat, but the patient says he must eat, we give him food, for the pasuk tells us*[39]*, "The heart knows the bitterness of its soul."*
>
> *Furthermore, Mar Rav Bar Ashi agrees with R' Yannai that if the patient says he does not need food, but even one doctor disagrees with him, then we give the person food.*
>
> *The general ruling is that when there is uncertainty in matters involving danger to life, we rule leniently.*[40]

Throughout the history of human society, there have been factions that have practiced fasting. Most often people have fasted for health reasons, that is, to cleanse the body, or for religious reasons. Fasting has also evolved as an expression of nonviolent protest and as a means of gaining attention and/or evoking feelings of guilt.

The observant Jewish patient who is ordered by a doctor to eat on a fast day struggles to the extreme with this mandate. Children from the youngest age are acclimated to the concept of fasting specifically in the context of the

---

[36] *Megillah 16b*
[37] *Sofrim, 21:3*
[38] *Yuma 82b*
[39] *Mishlei, 14:10*
[40] *Yuma 84b*

teshuvah process – to successfully achieve repentance. In their immaturity they will boast about how many hours they were able to go without food.

Yet, a person who is in treatment may be tampering with his life if he attempts to abide by Jewish law and fast. A patient who is in recovery may not be able to psychologically handle fasting.

A patient with an eating disorder called me *Erev Yom Kippur* [the eve]. He wanted me to confirm that he must follow the doctor's orders to eat on *Yom Kippur*. I explained that one could eat less than the prescribed measure of food prohibited by the Torah, so it would only involve a transgression of a rabbinic prohibition rather than a biblical prohibition. I then outlined the specific measurements entailed. The patient simply said, "If I have to measure my food I'd rather not eat." Undoubtedly, based on individual circumstances and the health risks to the patient, the situation would have to be resolved in an another way.

When the patient is not allowed to fast, it contradicts the essence of his religion, and he is overwhelmed by feelings of failure and defeat as he is exempted from a major obligation of the Jewish religion. He also cannot understand the dichotomy of thought in overruling Jewish law when he is actually fasting regularly on a daily basis.

The difficulty of this is compounded by the Torah's injunction to eat on *Erev Yom Kippur*. So important is this *mitzvah,* that the Talmud teaches[41] that whoever eats on *Erev Yom Kippur* it is as if he fasted on both the ninth and tenth days of Tishrei.

Another call that I received *Erev Yom Kippur* was from an inpatient facility in Arizona. The medical team had instructed the patient that, under no circumstances, would she be allowed to fast on *Yom Kippur*. I explained to the patient that she must follow the doctor's instructions precisely. The patient responded, "I feel horrible. I messed up so much in my life that I have to repent for, and now I'm messing up the repentance as well. I can't even do *Yom Kippur* right."

---

[41] *Berachos 8b*

"Guilt is an essential part of being a feeling, responsible person. It is a tool of the conscience that, in its undistorted form, registers discomfort and self-reproach if we've done something to violate our personal or social code of ethics. Guilt helps to keep our moral compass working, and because it feels so painful it dominates our attention until we do something to relieve it. Unfortunately, our sense of guilt can easily give us false readings about the impact of our actions."[42]

GOSSIP

You shall not be a gossipmonger among your people[43]

One of the prohibitions of *lashon hora* includes relating negative or disparaging, but truthful, remarks about another person. However, there are times when a person is obligated to reveal certain information.

The prohibition of *lashon hora*,[44] also extends to speaking ill of oneself. As a source of this law, the Chofetz Chaim cites *Yeshayah 6:5* where the Prophet Yeshayah is punished for speaking critically of himself by saying, in the presence of Hashem, that both he and his people are of impure lips.

The Chofetz Chaim states that if someone is considering marriage, but is unaware of **SUBSTANTIAL** faults in his prospective partner, and he would refuse the *shidduch* if he knew, one should reveal the information. This obligation is mandatory on anyone who knows about the problem, including the parents of the young man or woman.

In his *sefer*,[45] the Chofetz Chaim elaborates at length on the definition of

---

[42] Susan Forward, PhD, *Emotional Blackmail*
[43] *Vayikra 19:16*
[44] *Mekor HaChaim, Chapter 1*
[45] *Sefer Chofetz Chaim, Hilchos Rechilus, Klal 9:3*

"substantial" faults, which includes a health problem, a deficiency in one's spiritual point of view, or a substantial inadequacy in Torah knowledge.

The ramifications of this *halachah* extend even further with the need to fill out school and camp applications that specifically question the candidates as to whether or not they have an eating disorder. Principals and administrators have explained that they don't want to take responsibility for a student or camper who may require emergency medical attention.

I am asked all the time whether one is obligated to reveal an eating disorder condition on these applications. There is, of course, the undeniable probability that the applicant will be rejected if the truth is told. It is never a wise precedent, though, to begin any relationship – whether with a school, a camp, or on a personal level – based on withheld information.

There is a point to be made, sometimes, that an individual with an eating disorder may actually be helped in the therapeutic process by being able to strive for the goal of going to an "out-of-town" seminary, making a change in setting, or having a new relationship.

Understandably, the degree to which the individual's illness has manifested itself will have a bearing on the disclosure that is necessary. Sometimes there is a single episode of a failure to eat and intense exercise that is precipitated by a stressor. If that pressure is resolved then there is no progression that could develop into an illness.

If the behavior becomes more deeply ingrained, however – even if it never becomes a life-threatening situation nor do serious medical complications develop — there would be a need for disclosure. Some individuals do well in outpatient care. Others, however, may need an inpatient program with more intensive support to recover from their eating disorder.

Societal or communal factors may also have a bearing on whether or not to conceal a person's eating disorder. The contention is that in a large school there will be a given percentage of students who have eating disorders, to a greater or lesser degree.

A community in the Midwest had invited me to be the scholar-in-residence for a week. I was contacted by an administrator of one of the larger area high schools to speak to the students and include the topic of eating disorders and the Torah perspective during the talk. I readily agreed.

As soon as I was picked up at the airport, I received an urgent call from a different member of the administration who frantically pleaded, "Whatever you do, do not mention anything about eating disorders."

Obviously, even though there was definitely a concern about eating disorders among the school's students, there was an unwillingness to reveal this in a public forum.

WASTE NOT, WANT NOT

Do not destroy its trees by swinging an axe against them, for from it you will eat[46]

-Mitzvah 529

Although the original Torah prohibition of *bal tashchis* (not to destroy) is derived from the *pasuk* that prohibits soldiers from destroying the fruit trees around a city they are besieging, our Sages have expanded this to include any wanton or needless destruction of anything on earth.

The Rambam[47] summarizes the prohibition as follows:

Not only the trees, rather whoever breaks vessels and rents garments, destroys a building and obstructs a wellspring, or wastes food in a destructive way transgresses the mitzvah of bal tashchis.

---

[46] *Devarim, 20:19*
[47] *Hilchos Melachim, 6:8-10*

The Sefer HaChinuch makes an interesting connection between character development and avoiding even the slightest waste. In discussing the root of this *mitzvah*, the author writes that it is in order to "teach our souls to love the good and the useful … and we will distance ourselves from everything evil and from all manner of destruction …"

Rabbi Siman-Tov David[48] takes the prohibition of *bal tashchis* one step further. The author establishes a concept of *bal tashchis al gufo* – "wasting one's body." Consequently, he states, one who has not started to smoke cigarettes should certainly not allow himself to become addicted to this habit because it is injurious to his health. In his footnotes, he cites the Ravad, who states that one who eats things that are detrimental to his health is a *poshei'a* (transgressor or offender). He is harming his body and his soul.

The prohibition of *bal tashchis* concerning food is another among the many Torah precepts that are introduced to children at an early age. At the Passover Seder, in fact, when there is the custom to spill a drop of wine for each of the Ten Plagues as they are spoken aloud, we are cautioned that it should only be a minute drop and no more, so that we do not transgress the prohibition of "*bal tashchis.*"[49]

Children who begin severe dieting or have an eating disorder are facing an even more comprehensive challenge than minute morsels of food going to waste. They have uneaten lunches and snacks that they cannot bring home at the end of the school day, because it will expose their issues with food. They may try to dispose of the food in the school garbage cans, but will not be able to evade the eventual questioning.

The conflict is made even tougher when we take into account an interesting – and ancient – tradition that is practiced in most Jewish homes. When there is a need to throw out bread, we kiss it and wrap it before disposing of the bread. This is to demonstrate the great reverence that we have for food and the regret that we feel when we have to throw out food. This is

---

[48] *Al Pachim Ketanim, Laws of Bal Tashchis*
[49] *Ibid.*

an extreme contradiction to the individual who is not merely discarding a piece of bread. She is disposing of an entire dinner and is taking every precaution to avoid being discovered carrying out this deed.

The patient with the eating disorder, in fact, experiences guilt feelings that are far-reaching.

The word *anorexia* means "lack of appetite," yet people who have anorexia nervosa are actually hungry and preoccupied with food. "They study diets and calories; they collect recipes; and they prepare elaborate meals for others; they hoard, conceal, and deliberately waste food."[50]

Bulimics are pained when they are compelled to purge an entire meal that they have just ingested. In response to the question of whether there was any sense of guilt, one bulimic reflected, "I feel very guilty about wasting food, which I feel like I do a lot. I usually get hit with a pretty big wave of guilt and sadness after I regurgitate, but after an hour or so it passes."[51]

Oftentimes, the anorexic or bulimic is plagued with issues of self-worth. Many people with eating disorders feel that eating is a waste of food. "We don't feel that we are worth nourishing." One person says, "In the throes of an eating disorder, I would never take seconds – even if I was still hungry. I didn't want to 'waste' food that could be used to fuel someone else – someone more worthy of living."[52]

The patient with an eating disorder agonizes about taking too much food. The patient in recovery notes, "I needed to allow myself to 'waste' food. I needed to learn how to listen to my body, to figure out when I was hungry and full, because I had lost that connection. I needed to learn to believe that it was okay to miscalculate and take too much. It reinforced the belief that it's okay not to be perfect." Or, as one anorexic wrote, "Yeah, I waste

---

[50] *Merck Manual of Medical Information*
[51] *Everything Too*
[52] *Wellsphere Newsletter*

food, and I don't even bat an eyelash. I refuse to give food the power to shame me anymore."[53]

Time and again, a patient who had a severe manifestation of this illness, requiring frequent trips to doctors, hospital stays and a total disruption of a "normal" life, will make the startling statement, "I've wasted half of my life."

GOOD AND EVIL

Woe is to me because of my Creator, woe is to me because of my evil inclination

-Berachos 61a

As we know, man's life on this earth is characterized as a struggle between the *yetzer hora* – the Evil Inclination and the *yetzer tov* – the Good Inclination. The task of the *yetzer tov* is to influence us to go in the ways of Torah, to perform the *mitzvos,* and to raise our spiritual level closer to Hashem. The objective of the Evil Inclination, however, is to lure us away from the true path of Torah and to bring about our spiritual downfall.

Unfortunately, many people erroneously believe that the patient with an eating disorder is simply surrendering to his own personal *yetzer hora.* They do not realize the overwhelmingly pervasive influence of an eating disorder. It is an illness that completely dominates one's life.

We cannot just tell the person with the eating disorder, "Why don't you stop this ridiculous behavior and start eating? You can see for yourself what it's doing to you." One anorexic explained to me, "I hate it so much. Why am I not letting go? I can't. I really can't. You wake up every morning and

---

[53] *Ibid.*

you sometimes feel like you don't want to live. It's such hard work to live like this. But I'm petrified to let go."

Eating disorders include extreme emotions, attitudes, and behaviors surrounding weight and food issues. They are serious emotional and physical problems that can have life-threatening consequences for females and males alike.[54]

The complexity of an eating disorder removes any voluntary control from the sufferer. It is an alien being that dominates the person's body and mind. What is most frightening about this disease is the knowledge that we are all vulnerable. Eating disorders cross all social, economic, cultural, and educational backgrounds. They affect children in elementary schools and senior citizens as well; people who are poor as well as those who are wealthy; individuals in small towns and big cities.

Recovery often requires a mental health team, medical personnel in various specialties, and a nutritionist who all work cooperatively to restore the patient's physical good health and mental equilibrium.

In discussing biopsychiatry, Dr. Russell Marx writes the following: "The study of neurochemistry reveals how tiny molecules interact with brain cells and trigger not just physical activity, but thoughts, moods, and feelings as well. Through these and other discoveries, we have become more aware of how the body's biological malfunctions can lead to emotional disturbances ..."[55]

Concerning self-control and addictions, researchers indicate,[56] "You don't have to have every element of an addictive personality, or to be emotionally disturbed to become trapped by addictive behavior. All it takes is your brain's memory, or imprint of an experience with some activity or substance that was inordinately comforting, release-giving, enjoyable. Later, when

---

[54] *National Eating Disorders Association*
[55] Dr. Russell Marx, *It's Not Your Fault*, pg. 12
[56] Dr. Arnold Washton and Donna Boundy, MSW, *Will Power Is Not Enough*

you experience a high level of stress, as we all do at one time or other, you may be unconsciously compelled to seek that substance or activity again. Without your even realizing it, a vicious cycle can be set in motion. Actual bio-chemical effects on the brain can reinforce the dependency."

> *The Talmud recounts*[57] *that Shimon HaTzaddik once stated, "In all my days I never ate of the Asham offering of a Nazir* who became tamei — ritually unclean, except for one. There was a Nazir from the south who had become ritually unclean. I saw that he had beautiful eyes and was good-looking. His hair was beautifully arranged in curls. I said to him, 'My son, why did you find it necessary to destroy this beautiful hair of yours?'*
>
> *"He replied to me, 'I was a shepherd in the city where I lived. I once went to fill a pail of water from the well, and I saw my reflection in the water. At that moment my Evil Inclination overtook me and wanted to banish me from the world [by bringing me to sin]. I said to the yetzer hora, "You wicked one, why are you arrogant in a world that is not yours with a person who in the future will be consumed by the dust of the earth? I swear by the Temple that I shall shave you for the sake of Heaven."'*
>
> *Immediately R' Shimon stood up and kissed him on his head. He said to him, "May there be many more like you who undertake a vow of Nezirus in Israel like you."*

One should not confuse the influence of the Evil Inclination with the influence of an eating disorder. Eating disorders can hardly be considered within the realm of listening to the *yetzer hora*. It is a total upheaval of the body, mind and soul. The physical appearance of the patient with an eating disorder becomes altered and at times unsightly. The person's hair thins,

---

[57] *Nedarim 9b*

*A *Nazir* is a man who dedicates himself to God by taking a vow (for a specified period of time or for a lifetime) to abstain from wine, to never cut his hair and to avoid corpses.

the eyebrows and eyelashes fall out, teeth can turn black, and the skin turns yellow. The facial features become distorted, to the point of asymmetry, and the body becomes skeletal and gaunt. Any trace of beauty or attractiveness vanishes as the effects of the eating disorder insidiously invade the body.

RETURN TO ME

"They shall confess their sin that they committed"[58]
"Return to Me and I will return to you! says Hashem"[59]

Teshuvah, translated as "repentance," is actually derived from the root word meaning "to return." In order for an individual to achieve true *teshuvah*, he must go through a sequence of stages that are outlined by the Rambam in *Hilchos Teshuvah*.

There is *hakaras hachet* – recognition of one's sin. This is an act of intelligence and moral conscience that involves the individual acknowledging that specific behaviors of his are sinful.

The individual must feel sincere *charatah*, or remorse, for past commission of his sin.

Azivas hachet refers to the action of desisting from the pattern of sinful action to which one has become accustomed. It involves actually stopping the sinful action and making a firm pledge never to commit the sinful act again.

And *viduy* – confession of the sin and the request for forgiveness.

---

[58] *Bamidbar, 5:7*
[59] *Malachi, 3:7*

The Rambam teaches us that as part of the *Viduy* a person should include the words: "I will never again repeat this transgression."[60]

The Mabit[61] asks: What happens if the person is not successful, and does repeat her transgression in the future?

The *Mabit* maintains that the *teshuvah* remains valid and genuine. His opinion is that repetition of the *aveiroh* (transgression) does not in any way indicate that one's original *teshuvah* was insincere. The person did, in fact, make a *kabbalah al ha'asid* – a resolution not to sin in the future; he did have regret; there was an abandonment of the *aveiroh*. The Godly soul actually remained firm, says the Mabit, but the animalistic soul within the person yielded to temptation.

Teshuvah for the individual caught in the clutches of an eating disorder presents particular difficulty. Indisputably, the individual has done nothing wrong; he is ill and is considered to be in the category of "one who is under duress is exempted from performing a *mitzvah*".[62]

Nevertheless, eating disorder patients feel hindered in their ability to fulfill certain *mitzvos* and burdened by their transgression of Torah prohibitions. They are driven by a need to repent and to know that they are forgiven by Hashem. As we have mentioned, though, the components of proper *teshuvah* include a resolution to desist from perpetrating the sin in the future. As with anyone recovering from addiction, although the individual may try with all his might to avoid reverting to his addictive behavior, there is always the possibility of a relapse. When the individual experiences such a setback, he begins to question his coping skills and his ability to ever rid himself of the illness. This results in further self-doubt and leads to depression. Ann Wilson Schaef points out that the addict's depression is related to his belief that he *ought* to be able to control everything – a goal that he will inevitably be unable to reach.[63]

---

[60] *Hilchos Teshuva, Halachah 1*
[61] *Bais Elokim*
[62] *Bava Kamma 28b*
[63] *When Society Becomes an Addict*

Oftentimes a bulimic patient has remarked to me: "I know that my habits are sinful. Even before I purge, I regret my compulsion to purge and resolve that I will try harder to discontinue this behavior."

The Talmud states,[64] "If a person says 'I will sin and then I will repent, I will sin and then I will repent,' he is not provided from Heaven to repent."

The great R' Yisroel of Rizhin offers a novel interpretation of this statement. He asks: If the individual is so attuned to his spiritual responsibilities that before he sins he is already concerned about his ability to totally repent, why is he not given the opportunity to achieve complete *teshuvah?*

R' Yisroel of Rizhin answers that a person needs *siyata d'shmaya* (Divine Assistance) in his quest for *teshuvah.* However, this individual who is contemplating his repentance even as he commits the *aveiroh* has no need for this extra Divine Assistance. He is already consumed with an overwhelming sense of guilt and self-reproach that is binding in the *teshuvah* process.

"A person who embarks on a journey of serving Hashem should not become distracted by the lack of total success. He must understand that every bit of effort that he expends to reach perfection, brings him one step closer to his goal. Even when he still feels entrapped by his inclination he must concentrate on going forward, and reassure himself that every step is bringing him closer to freedom. Eventually, he, too, will see the shore on the horizon. [65]

---

[64] *Yuma 85b*
[65] Rabbi S. Wagschal, *Practical Guide to Teshuvah*

PREVENTION: A TEN-STEP PROGRAM

MIRI'S STORY

The principal of one of the local schools called one morning. She was concerned because one of their popular students in the 10th grade, Miri, had lost an abnormal amount of weight. They noticed that she had become somewhat withdrawn, and her hair was thinning. The principal remarked, "She has probably jumped on the bandwagon to become skeletal thin," and it was assumed that it was a "classic" case of anorexia.

I asked how long this had been going on, and the principal speculated that it had probably begun shortly after the beginning of the school year. She explained that, since the family was dysfunctional, she had been asked to contact me.

Miri came in with her parents the next evening, and we talked. She volunteered information about her friends, her classes, and her interests. I guided the conversation toward her eating disordered behavior and tried to assess the threat to her health in her present condition. Towards the end of the session, I casually asked Miri if there had been any unsettling changes in her life at the beginning of the school year.

She replied in the negative, although she did tell me that she had moved in with friends of the family. She explained that it was difficult to live at home because of overcrowded conditions and some issues between her and her parents.

"How are things where you are now?" I asked.

"Fine," she said. She told me there was a girl her own age in the family, who had become a good friend. She seemed happy about having more space, and mentioned that she even had her own room. Miri then quickly changed the subject and went on to talk about some of her future plans.

I wondered at her abrupt change of subject, but I let the thought go. I was happy that she was thinking about the future and had ideas and dreams.

A few days later, Miri's parents came back with her for another session. Miri seemed troubled, when we began to talk. I asked her whether there was anything specific she would like to bring up. She said, "You know, the last time I was here you asked how I was doing at my friend's home."

Tears began to roll slowly down her face. "I have never told this to anybody," she sobbed, "but there is some form of abuse occurring in the house. I have seen it sometimes and I am traumatized. I can't tell my best friend, because she believes I don't know about it. I am ashamed to tell anyone I want to leave and go to a different home, because they may think that I am never happy, no matter where I am. I am also afraid that, if anybody ever finds out about this, not only will I lose one of my good friends, but her parents will be very angry and will attempt to discredit me."

Needless to say, I now had the missing piece of the puzzle. Studies show that individuals in Miri's situation often starve themselves because they feel they don't deserve anything good. They look to gain control of their surroundings in the only way they feel they can - by restricting their food intake.

I asked Miri's permission to pursue this matter and take care of it in a very confidential and discreet manner. I outlined the steps I would like to take and she consented.

Together with the principal and Miri's parents, I worked to remove Miri from that home. We were successful in finding a relative, whose home provided a wholesome and nurturing environment for Miri.

With the encouragement and assistance of some caring individuals, Miri progressed on the road to recovery. I am happy to report that when she finished high school, she was able to fulfill a dream she had never thought possible and spent a successful year in seminary abroad, in Israel.

PREVENTION: A TEN-STEP PROGRAM

KNOW YOUR CHILD

Major keys to preventing the development of an eating disorder in a family member are to "know" children, to understand their individual nature and to be attuned to the nuances in behaviors. Very often, there are initial subtle hints that are actually a call for help. If the cry is not heard, or ignored, the child may become frustrated, which may develop into an at-risk behavior.

> *To comprehend the meaning of eating disorders, we must understand their origins. Eating disorders are a complex negative interpretation of one's role in life.*[1]

Reb Simcha Bunim of Psischa questions the wordage in the *pasuk*,[2] "*Kamayim hapanim lapanim kein lev ha'adam la'adam* – As water reflects a face back to a face, so one's heart is reflected back to him by another." Why, he asks, do we talk about seeing one's reflection in water? If a person wishes to see his reflection he usually looks in the mirror.

His answer provides us with a unique insight into the human condition. We can see our reflection in the mirror, even if the mirror is 100 feet away. For example, if we enter a great hall, where there is a mirror on the opposite wall we will be able to see our reflection. However, if we want to see our reflection in a body of water, we must bend over and bring our face within inches of the water. Similarly, if we wants to understand the world of a person suffering from an eating disorder, we cannot observe it from the distance, in our wholesome state with a healthy attitude toward eating and body image. We must come very close to this individual, so that we can truly relate to this person and his or her situation.

Hundreds of people would flock to a renowned rabbi for his counsel and blessing. Yet, the rabbi had a practice of taking a break between each meet-

---

[1] Peggy Claude-Pierre, *The Secret Language of Eating Disorders*
[2] *Mishlei*, 27:19

ing. The *shammash* (sexton) asked why it was necessary to prolong the wait of the petitioners with a break. The rabbi explained, "When the shoemaker comes in, I have to take off my rabbinic frock and put on the shoemaker's apron. I place the hammer in my hand, the nails in my mouth, so that I can see the situation from his standpoint and give him the proper advice. When he leaves, and the baker is coming in, I have to first remove the shoemaker's apron and don the baker's hat and apron dusted with flour so that I can see his problems in life through his eyes."

- Be alert to your child's inner needs
- Be aware of anxiety and guilt feelings associated with separation
- Be sensitive to any feelings of shame the child may have with regard to her looks
- Take note of any indications of low self-esteem
- Be attuned to signs of depression or disappointment
- Notice expressions of resentment, anger, or a loss of control
- Intuit any feelings of powerlessness that a child may be feeling.

EARLY DETECTION OF AN EATING DISORDER

Pay close attention to the members of your family. Notice if someone begins to skip meals, if a child seems to be bringing home the same lunch that she took to school, or the teacher mentions that the child doesn't seem to be eating his lunch or is playing with his food. Take note if your teenager pays unusual attention to the nutrition panel of foods, weighs herself constantly, or engages in other activities that show undue concern with weight or body image. Be alert to any behaviors that may seem strange; tune in to conversations or offhand remarks made in the home.

Spouses have been known to be completely unaware of their partner's anorexic behavior. A husband began to notice that his wife's teeth were turning dark and suggested that she use a whitening toothpaste. However, her teeth began to get darker and darker. He ultimately accompanied her to the dentist, who immediately recognized the drastic effects of an eating disorder. Her husband had no idea that his wife was severely anoretic.

PRESSURE

Daily life presents numerous challenges. Societal pressures of all sorts compound a difficult situation and may send a person over the edge. Adolescents are particularly vulnerable to peer pressure, competition and rivalry. There is pressure to succeed, pressure to outdo, pressure to be at the top. In addition, although much effort has been made on the part of educational institutions to alleviate academic demands, there is still a significant emphasis on achievement of excellence. The high school experience, especially, is primarily focused on superior grades, exclusive cliques, and special recognition. These pressures can become overwhelming and anxiety-producing, sometimes precipitating an eating disorder.

> *There is the pressure. You feel, am I only worth something if I'm thin? There is this society thing, like, that to be thin you're in control, or to be thin means that you're accomplishing a lot more. And you start thinking to yourself, "Wait a minute. What about the other qualities that I have? Am I not worth it?" So then you automatically start to prove to them, "Oh, you think I can't show you what I can do? Let me show you what I can do!"* [3]

Sometimes these pressures grow even more complex. Beginning from birth, there is a compulsion to get into the school of choice, then there is a need to get into the "right" high school, followed by the struggle to be accepted into the "best" institution of higher learning. The social scene becomes even more competitive when young people begin the process of seeking a part-

---

[3] Rabbi Dovid Goldwasser, *Starving to Live*

ner in marriage – where differences in the male/female ratio and multiple factors produce megadoses of anxiety and stress.

It is important to be able to recognize the various anxiety disorders, which can be classified in six categories: generalized anxiety disorder, panic disorders, agoraphobia, phobias, obsessive-compulsive disorder, and post-traumatic stress disorder.

Rabbi Moshe Chaim Luzzato (1707-1746) in the *Path of the Just* illustrates the devastating effect of stress with an interesting insight. He notes that Pharaoh's intent in subjecting the Jewish nation to torturous labor was twofold. Not only did he mean to deprive the people of their leisure so that they would not oppose him or rise up against him, but he wanted to strip their hearts and mind of the ability to think clearly.

THE FAMILY UNIT

A recent survey defined a wholesome family as one where the parents strive to instill values, trust, security, morals and open communication among its members, and include a spiritual component or affiliation.

To be sure, a fair amount of attention needs to be focused on each child and his personal development. Young people have been found to act out in a number of ways when the family is dysfunctional, there is lack of unity or the focus of attention shifts to a single member or even an outsider currently residing with the family. Disordered eating can be one of those ways.

Sibling rivalry is present in most families, to a greater or lesser degree. My own research has shown that prime candidates for the development of an eating disorder usually grow up in situations where an older/younger brother/sister outshines them or is given extra attention.

Siblings can never be compared to each other, nor can our expectations be the same for all. The Rambam states that just as our appearances are different, so too are our mind-sets and thought processes different. Each child has a completely different set of strengths and positive attributes which must always be highlighted.

The catastrophic effects of favoring one child over another are narrated in the Talmud[4]. *"L'olam al yeshaneh adam bno bein habanim ...* — A person should never treat one child different than another, for because of two silver coins' weight of fine wool that Yaakov gave Yosef more than he gave to his other sons, his brothers became jealous of him, and their jealousy intensified until Yosef was sold by his brothers into slavery and our forefathers ultimately descended into Egypt."

PARENTAL PERSUASION

Parents' behaviors and attitudes deeply affect their children, even in dysfunctional homes, or where parents are abusive. Children tend to emulate their parents' actions and attitudes. Constantly talking about weight and diet, or commenting on how thin or overweight so-and-so is, sends a strong message to children that may have undesirable results. An extreme fixation on calorie counting or an overzealous exercise program has similarly detrimental implications for children. It is highly inadvisable to talk about food being good or bad or fattening.

You can say, "Oh, it's so good that you want a rice cake ... it's so healthy." You could encourage healthy foods. There's nothing wrong with encouraging it. But there's something wrong if a parent always says, "Don't eat this," or "Don't buy that." I see little kids, at snack-time, walking around with Weight Watcher's snacks and I cry ... Why should

---

[4] *Shabbos 10b*

a nine-year-old have to be eating something with Nutrasweet in it? Her peer is eating a danish!"[5]

A parent's offhand comment or remark – negative or positive – may impact profoundly on a child's self-esteem. Children innately seek their parents' approval. I have had people in their 60s and 70s come in for counseling because they are still dealing with parental disapproval or dissatisfaction.

Comments concerning body image and weight must be carefully monitored. A seemingly innocuous remark like, "Are you sure you want another doughnut?" can be devastating to a vulnerable adolescent. Parents should not impose their personal prejudices or misconceptions about body image on their offspring by observing, "You could lose a few pounds." Mealtime should not become a battleground at home.

EDUCATION

The Talmud[6] discusses the parent's obligations to his child, which includes teaching him how to swim. Our Sages have broadened this definition to encompass equipping the child with life-coping skills.

Talk to your children about:

- The importance of eating well-balanced meals three times a day
- The danger of trying to change one's body shape by drastic dieting
- Being comfortable with their weight and/or shape
- The importance of exercise in moderation for a healthy body
- The injustice of prejudices based on weight or body image

---

[5] Rabbi Dovid Goldwasser, *Starving to Live*
[6] *Kiddushin 29a*

We have allowed an unkind, sometimes inhumane, interpretation of eating disorders to prevail, and that interpretation has permitted numerous innocent fatalities.[7]

SELF-EXPRESSION

The Talmud[8] cites Rav Ami and Rav Ashi who debate the meaning of *"da'agah b'lev ish yashchenah."* Rav Ami says that one who is worried should remove the worry from his mind; Rav Ashi differs and says he should share his concerns with others. It is explained that people have various ways of dealing with their fears and uncertainties. We are all different in nature and temperament, and the coping mechanisms for each individual must be respected and validated.

Therefore, if children need to talk about what is bothering them, they should feel free to be able to express themselves. Children should not be told that they are foolish to worry, nor should their concerns be dismissed as nonsense.

If feelings are not allowed to be expressed in a family, the child's true self – her emotional reality – is by definition rejected. This rejection of herself is experienced as a profound abandonment just as if she had been rejected by overly hostile, unstable parents.[9]

---

[7] Peggy Claude-Pierre, *The Secret Language of Eating Disorders*

[8] *Yuma 75a*

[9] Arnold Washton, PhD and D. Boundy, MSW, *The Addictive Family: Will Power Is Not Enough*

INNER BEAUTY

The Torah tells us[10] that Hashem said to the *malachim*, *"Naaseh adam b'tzalmeinu,"* and our Sages explain that man was created in the image of God. In all our heterogeneity, we are all equally creations of God, and thus we are inherently beautiful. In fact, disparaging remarks concerning another's appearance or looks is considered to be a transgression of a negative Torah commandment.

Although it is true that reference is made to beauty throughout the Talmud and rabbinic literature, in reality it is focused on the inner beauty of the individual. The Vilna Gaon notes that the Torah comments on the beauty of the Matriarchs – Sarah, Rivka and Rochel – and contrasts it with the statement of Shlomo HaMelech[11] that beauty is vain. The Gaon explains that contrary to physical beauty, which is only skin-deep, the *Imahos* possessed a spiritual beauty that radiated outward from within. Such beauty is noteworthy.

COMMUNICATION

It is vital to develop and maintain open lines of communication within the family. The atmosphere in the home should be non-judgmental, allowing all members to express their true feelings. Thoughts and opinions should be validated; they should not be negated or dismissed.

The open exchange of ideas enables individuals to work through many of their difficulties and challenges. Once the channels of communication break down, however, people resort to more drastic means of getting their ideas and feelings across.

---

[10] *Bereishis, 1:26*
[11] *Mishlei, 31:30*

The Torah tells us,[12] "*Divrei chachamim b'nachas nishma'im* – the gentle words of the wise are heard," i.e., words spoken in a kind manner are listened to by others. Rabbi Meir Shapiro (founder and dean of the renowned Yeshivas Chachmei Lubin in Poland) points out that this was stated with regard to the performance of *mitzvos*. Certainly one should be heedful to speak gently when addressing other critical matters. When someone speaks in a pleasant, caring and considerate voice, his message is much more likely to be heard. It will also help to eliminate any defensiveness on the part of the listener.

Our Sages tell us similarly, "*Devarim hayotzim min halev nichnasim el halev* – Words that are spoken sincerely from the heart go into the heart." Speak honestly, from the bottom of your heart. Show the individual with an eating disorder that you care about his well-being. Do not convey reproach or fault-finding when you talk to him.

Communicate your points effectively, in a concise manner, as stated in *Koheles*[13], "Let your words be few." Most people employ an automatic cut-off switch when they feel that the "lecture" has exceeded their capacity to listen. Edit your comments; consider which ideas are most important to convey and omit those that may be superfluous.

The Torah commands,[14] "*V'lo sonu ish es amiso* – You shall not aggrieve your fellow man." Our Sages tell us that verbal insults or abuse, as well as exhibiting a facial grimace, a motion or a gesture that makes the other person feel uncomfortable, are all covered by this prohibition.

Be careful not to be critical or say things that will hurt another person's feelings. Do not remind him of other occasions when he did not listen and the result was disastrous. Insults are usually counterproductive. Rather than being helpful in the person's recovery, verbal abuse tends to prompt an escalation in the at-risk behavior.

---

[12] *Koheles, 9:17*
[13] *5:1*
[14] *Vayikra, 25:17*

Be a good listener. Be attentive. Don't interrupt. Allow the other person to finish conveying her thoughts. Make sure to address the points that she has raised in an orderly manner, as we learn,[15] *"Omer al rishon rishon v'al acharon acharon* — [a learned person] discusses first things first and last things last."

PRAYER

We need spiritual guidance, like they have for the secular world. A twelve-step program – twelve steps to finding God in their way. They're always coming up today with the answers: a spiritual leader, believe in doctors, prayer helps.[16]

The Talmud tells us[17] that the world stands on three pillars, one of which is *tefillah* – prayer. In explaining the *mitzvah* of *tefillah*, the Rambam[18] states: "A person should plead in prayer daily and say the praises of the Holy One ... request his needs ... and offer praise and thanks to Hashem for all the good that He has already given him..."

Prayer is a service of the heart. It is the medium through which we praise Hashem and thank Him for His blessings. But it is also the vehicle for our requests and pleas for understanding, success and good health.

Prayers truly from the heart open all the doors in heaven –
Rabbi Nachman of Breslov

---

15 *Pirkei Avos, 5:7*
16 Rabbi Dovid Goldwasser, *Starving to Live*
17 *Pirkei Avos, 1:2*
18 *Hilchos Tefillah, 1:2*

GETTING HELP

ALIZA'S STORY

It was a bitter winter day, the eve of Chanukah. As I prepared the *menorah* and its wicks for the occasion, I contemplated the deep symbolism of the *menorah's* radiant light, representing the light of Torah that illuminates our long exile and guides us through all the vicissitudes of life.

As often happens, the tranquility and my thoughtful reflections were interrupted by the loud ringing of the phone. A community activist with whom I am acquainted was calling with an urgent request.

A 23-year-old woman named Aliza, who was suffering from an eating disorder, had been checked into Columbia Presbyterian Hospital's program. She was in desperate need of encouragement and support at this time. Once I was filled in on some other pertinent details, I assured the caller that I was leaving immediately, as time was of the essence.

Upon entering the hospital room, I was shocked at the patient's state of emaciation and frailty. I introduced myself and, although she was barely able to sit up, it was apparent that Aliza was very much interested in meeting me and wanted to have a meaningful conversation.

After I talked with her for quite a while and covered various topics related to eating disorders and recovery, I prepared to take my leave. I noticed then that Aliza seemed disconcerted and had something on her mind. She hesitated for a moment and then said in a curious tone, "I thought you were going to talk to me about God."

I was surprised and somewhat taken aback by her unexpected remark. I explained that, truthfully, I had come simply to see what I could do to assist in her recovery. However, I stated, I would be happy to discuss with her any issues concerning God and spirituality.

Aliza began to question me about the concept of this world and the here-after. In fact, she had a slew of questions – particularly about Heaven. It soon became clear that Aliza was tormented by the fear that she might possibly forfeit her opportunity to "enter into Heaven." Aware of the severity of the transgression for one who commits suicide, Aliza wanted to know what technically constituted suicide. She was distressed by the possibility that a person might be held accountable for possibly hastening his or her death when they became ill and did not take care of their health.

I tried to assuage her worries by clarifying the importance of each person's obligation to attempt to fulfill his *bein adam l'atzmo* — potentialities in life, and to improve his relation with his Maker, *bein adam laMakom*. I made it clear to her that any effort we make, even if we have not achieved our ultimate goal, is acknowledged; every step that we take to come closer to Hashem and to be a better person is rewarded.

We spoke about the person who is conflicted – the individual who tries his best and is determined to escape from the grips of this illness, but finds that willpower alone is sometimes not enough.

I elaborated on the verse, "*Harachaman hu yanchileinu yom shekulo shabbos umenucha l'chayei ha'olamim* – May He cause us to inherit the day which will be completely a Sabbath and rest day for eternal life," recited in the *Birchas HaMazon*, Grace After Meals. Our Sages tell us that this is an al-lusion to the World-to-Come, a world that will be completely good and peaceful.

Aliza sadly recounted that she had experienced a vast amount of pain and anguish over the last few years, which had been overwhelmingly depressing. The assurance that the challenges a person suffers in this world would ulti-mately grant serenity in the World-to-Come particularly affected Aliza. She pensively remarked, "If the place we arrive at after 120 years on this earth is indeed a better place, then perhaps this world could be more bearable."

Preoccupied with that thought, Aliza inquired as to whether I could suggest any further reading on this topic. I made a few suggestions, including the

Sefer Tehillim, the Book of Psalms, which expresses every human emotion.

A few days later, when she was permitted telephone time, Aliza called to proudly report that she had been avidly reading the various texts that I had suggested. I was happy to hear that she sounded a lot better and that she was deriving inspiration from these books and developing a more positive outlook on life. Even more pleasing was her information that she was re-discovering her Jewish roots.

Another week or two elapsed before I heard from Aliza again. I could hear a note of astonishment in her voice as she related that she had been reading the *Tehillim* regularly because it provided her with a sense of serenity. On that particular day, she exclaimed, she encountered a verse *(Tehillim 119:71)* that so clearly articulated a feeling she had been unable to express: *"It is good for me that I was afflicted, so that I might learn Your statutes."*

It is said that all things happen for a reason. Aliza wistfully noted, "Had I never had this eating disorder, I might never have studied the Torah."

When she was finally in recovery and allowed to leave the hospital, Aliza had not only regained her health but she had also redeemed her soul. She began to actively pursue her interest in everything Jewish – reading, learning, meeting people. To this day, Aliza continues to make progress, physically and spiritually along her journey in life.

SOUND ADVICE

An oft-used phrase for those taking leave of each other, or ending a conversation, is *"zei gezunt* – be well." Its implied meaning is twofold: "I'm praying for you, that is, I pray that you should be well" and "take care of yourself; make sure that you stay well."

The Torah directs us *"v'nishmarten me'od l'nafshoseichem* – take great heed with your souls," and our Sages elaborate that this refers to taking extra care of one's health. One has to be aware of the health dangers that exist. One has to safeguard his health so that he should continue to be well, with the help from Above, of course.

If you ask the experts, they can tell you exactly which areas of our health need more attention. Unfortunately, we don't always follow their advice. Maimonides states, "The ability of a physician to prevent illness is a greater proof of his skills than his ability to cure someone who is already ill."

For some reason, when a situation arises that would benefit from medical attention, people seem to have many questions in Jewish law about the propriety of making a doctor appointment. Is it *frum?* Is it the right thing to do? Would it be a breach of *emunas Hashem* (faith in Hashem)? Couldn't I just recite *Tehillim* (Book of Psalms)?

Rabbi Yisroel Salanter, founder of the Mussar movement, notes that when a person begins to feel ill, the Evil Inclination speaks up and says: "Don't go to the doctor. You don't have to go. Wait for a while; you'll feel better. It costs money. It's a bother. It's embarrassing. The doctor once prescribed the wrong medicine. What do they know?"

That's not the way at all. The *yetzer hora* (Evil Inclination) wants to dissuade a person from fulfilling the Torah obligation to take care of himself. A person should not make his own determinations in areas of Jewish law. He should ask a *sheiloh* (question of Jewish law) of a competent rabbi.

A number of years ago, an unusual billboard caught my eye. In bold black letters on a white background, the American Dental Association starkly announced: "Ignore your teeth; they'll go away." Humorous, but the point was compelling.

The same is true with all aspects of health. To maintain our health, we must be constantly on guard. We have to look after ourselves.

On the Shabbos that precedes each new Jewish month, *Shabbos Mevarchim,* we recite the *Yehi Ratzon,* the special blessing for the new month, before the *Mussaf* prayer. Among our requests, we ask for *"chaim shel chilutz atzamos* – a life of strong bones."* Our commentaries explain that, according to the mystical books, bones are extremely important for providing life-giving essence to the body.

The question arises: Why do we come back month after month and ask once again for "strong bones"?

The answer is given that a life of health and strength requires regular observation and examination. We must assess ourselves every month to ensure that we are well and that all is as it should be. That is our obligation. We also ask Hashem for Heavenly Assistance so that the doctors, the social workers, and all the health care workers — His representatives in this world – can successfully help us in our quest for health and strength.

Maimonides *(Rambam Mishnah Torah, Hilchos Dei'os, Ch. 4)* presents clear-cut suggestions for healthy eating

- Eat only when hungry
- Drink when thirsty
- Do not keep eating until your stomach is full; eat approximately one-quarter less than the amount that it would take to fully satisfy a person
- Eat warming foods during the winter months; in the summer months eat cooling foods
- Do not drink with your meal, except for a small quantity of water mixed with wine
- Do not drink water to excess
- Always be seated while eating
- Be careful not to walk, exercise, or engage in any physically demanding activity until food has been properly digested.

IN GOD'S IMAGE: A SELF-ESTEEM TUTORIAL

A very interesting story is told of a famous *maggid* (itinerant speaker in pre-war Europe) who came to a particular city. The *maggid* in those days would travel from city to city, usually staying over Shabbos, and give a series of *drashos* (sermons) for which he would be compensated. The communities throughout Europe would look forward with anticipation to his expected recurring arrival. He was extremely talented and would deliver enlightening lectures that provided a Torah perspective on life. He was an accomplished orator with unique abilities to inspire his audiences.

When the *maggid* arrived it was already close to candle-lighting time on Friday afternoon. His first stop was at the home of one of the wealthiest people in the city. When the butler opened the door and saw the visitor, he immediately summoned his employer. The wealthy man warmly greeted the rabbi and inquired about the *maggid*'s needs.

"If I may," said the *maggid*, "I would like to borrow a thousand silver pieces. I will pay you back right after Shabbos." Although his benefactor silently wondered what the *maggid* would do with the silver pieces over Shabbos, since he could not possibly spend it, he refrained from asking. He had great respect for the *maggid* and unimpeachable faith in the wisdom of the sages *(emunas chachamim)*.

The man immediately went to his safe, removed the considerable sum of one thousand silver pieces and gave it to the *maggid*.

Friday night the *maggid* gave his first *drasha*. People had come for Shabbos from all the little villages surrounding the city to hear the *maggid*'s words of inspiration. His heartfelt words penetrated the hearts and minds of all who were there.

On *Shabbos* morning, the *maggid* spoke once again, and this time the number of people in attendance had doubled. People who could not spend the entire Shabbos in the city, but were thirsting for the words of the *maggid*, had walked long distances to listen to him speak. Then the *maggid* spoke one more time before *Shalosh Seudos*.

Right after *havdalah*, the *maggid* once again appeared at the door of the wealthy man's home to return the thousand silver pieces. His benefactor could not contain his curiosity, and he blurted out, "Rebbi, could you possibly explain to me why you needed these thousand silver pieces? After all, it was impossible for you to do anything with this money on Shabbos. And now you are returning the money to me immediately after Shabbos. Why did you borrow it?"

The *maggid* softly replied, "*Veil mit gelt redt men andersh* — if you have money you speak differently."

I often think about this story of the *maggid* and the thousand silver pieces. Is it the silver pieces that really make a difference? Or, do they represent the external factors to which we ascribe our abilities and our potential for success?

Our perception of self-esteem has somehow become erroneously dependent on the accoutrements of money, looks, property, and connections. But the *mishnah* in *Pirkei Avos (6:6)* specifically lauds the individual who is *makir es mekomo* –knows his own place. The *Tzemach Dovid* explains this to mean that one must identify his true status in life by recognizing and appreciating the unique qualities of *chachmah* (wisdom), *binah* (understanding) and *daas* (knowledge) with which Hashem has blessed him, and treasuring the talents he has been bequeathed by Hashem. A deficiency in the individual's perception of *makir es mekomo* would inherently constrain his growth and development throughout life. It would limit his efforts in fulfilling his potential and he would "feel" unable and inadequate to face life's challenges.

In the narrative of the *meraglim* (scouts) to the Jewish nation upon their return from the exploratory visit to Eretz Yisroel, they tell the people (*Bamidbar 13:33*), "*… and there we saw the giants .. and we were in our eyes as grasshoppers, and so were we in their eyes.*"

The spies acknowledged that they felt like grasshoppers *in their own eyes;* it was the way they appeared to themselves. It had very little to do with their actual size. The fact that they perceived themselves as grasshoppers caused them to believe that the giants identified them as grasshoppers as well!

The way we feel about our personal appearance is the way we are perceived. A positive self-image projects our true beauty and reflects the uniqueness of our inner and outer persona.

Hashem grants us life so that we can serve Him. True servitude to God is a lifelong climb up the mountain of proper thought and action. But as He has given us the mountain, so has He equipped us with apparatus for the climb.

Food is one of the blessings that Hashem bestows upon us. When a person appreciates Hashem's gift of abundant food, and utilizes it appropriately, it makes it easier for him to ascend in his levels of spirituality and achieve his ultimate goal in life. Such a person will be successful in his endeavors to attain happiness, self-satisfaction and spiritual perfection in this world and in the World-to-Come.

Points to remember:

- Establish a network of support
- Associate with positive people
- Do not listen to or accept negative comments
- Write down your successes
- Discover your strengths and use them
- Do not compare yourself with others
- Do not put yourself down
- Think and speak positively
- Reward yourself for doing well
- Recognize that mistakes are opportunities
- Accept compliments
- Understand what is in your control and what is not
- Smile!

The preeminent leader of Torah Jewry, Rabbi Elazar Shach (1898-2001) notes in a similar vein that the individual with poor self-image does not realize the significance of "*b'tzelem elokim asah es ha'adam* — God created man in His Image."

He asks: How could it be that Adam – who understood that Hashem's presence filled the entire world — "hid" from HaKadosh Baruch Hu after he sinned?

Further, asks Rabbi Shach, how is it possible that Cain — who spoke face-to-face with Hakadosh Baruch Hu – said to Him, "Am I then my brother's keeper?"

He explains that, in fact, Adam and Cain did realize the greatness of man. They appreciated the import of the *nishmas chaim* (living soul) that Hashem breathed into them. They understood that they were imbued with incredible potential and capability. They therefore mistakenly thought that they were perhaps even able to hide from Hashem.

We, however, sometimes make an even greater error in judgment. We do not know how great we are at all. We underestimate and/or devalue the unique abilities with which we have been imbued.

Many commentators expound on the *pasuk* in *Bereishis (1:26)* "*Na'aseh adam b'tzalmeinu k'dmuseinu.*" They ask: What does it mean that Hashem, the sole creator of the world, said, "Let **US** make man?"

Our Sages explain that we, human beings, are partners with Hakadosh Baruch Hu in creation. Hashem has entrusted us with the all-important mission of continuing to develop and grow in Torah and good deeds. He has instilled within us the unique talents and abilities to strive for the spiritual perfection of our being *(shleimus)* with the *neshamah* that He breathed into our body.

Hashem has faith in our power to successfully fulfill our purpose (*tafkid*) in this world, and this knowledge is meant to reinforce our own self-esteem and sense of worth.

In dealing with our personal self-esteem, we should give ourselves credit for the talents that we have and highlight our positive attributes. Our Sages adjure us (*Pirkei Avos 2:18*) "*Al tehei rasha b'fnei atzmecha* – Do not judge yourself to be a wicked person."

One should always keep in mind that one of the reasons given for standing with our feet together during *Shemone Esrei* and during *kedusha* is to invoke our similarity to *malachim* (angels). In the eyes of Hashem we are like *malachim*. We have that potential within us. Remember, we are partners in the creation!

It is told that when the great Rabbi Simcha Zissel of Kelm, one of the primary figures of the Mussar movement (1824-1898), would gently wake up his children in the morning, he would say to them, "Children you are sleeping while you have a kingdom to rule." He wanted to instill in his children the awareness and reinforce their recognition that Hashem empowered man to rule over His entire creation.

There are times, unfortunately, when parents unwittingly transfer their sense of insecurity to their children. How we speak to a child, for example, concerning his abilities or lack thereof, has the potential to either strengthen the child's self-esteem and position him for success, or the reverse.

The spiritual mentor of the Mir Rabbinical Seminary, Rabbi Yeruchem Levovitz (1875-1936) notes the importance of learning, developing and preparing for greatness in life. He cites the *pasuk (Shemos 2:10)*, "The boy [Moshe] grew up and she brought him to the daughter of Pharaoh ..."

Even somebody as prominent as Moshe Rabbeinu needed to be raised and nurtured in the appropriate environment to prepare him properly for his ultimate role in life as the leader of the Jewish nation. Although the Torah corroborates that he was the most humble of all men, his self-image was positively impacted by the years he spent in the palace of the king. That exposure cultivated his ability to take responsibility and command of *Klal Yisroel.*

It is essential for parents, teachers, and all adults who interact with young people to be sensitive to young people's sense of self and to make an effort to boost their self-esteem. I would like to suggest a few points for consideration.

- Love should be real and not tied to performance.
- Love should be total and unconditional.
- We should not tell a child he has failed if he has not lived up to "our" expectations.
- We must be careful not to label a child as "clumsy," "a disappointment" or "dumb."
- "What is the matter with you?" is a problematic question that is threatening to a child.
- We should never tell a child she is "hopeless"
- Avoid comparing siblings, students, or neighbors.
- Always draw attention to the positive; address the negative in a sensitive manner so that the young person will be able to accept it.

TEN STEPS TO GREATNESS

By Rabbi Avigdor Miller *

Do the following once a day:

1) Spend 30 seconds thinking of *olam haba* – the World to Come

2) Say once, "I love You, Hashem."

3) Perform a secret act of loving kindness

4) Be like Hashem Who lifts the humble; say something to encourage someone

5) Spend one minute contemplating what happened yesterday (*cheshbon hanefesh*)

6) At least one time during the day, for example during mealtimes, recognize that your actions are for the sake of Heaven (*l'shem Shamayim*).

7) Look into someone's face and think: "I'm seeing the image of Hashem."

8) Just like Hashem's face shines on us, give someone a big smile

9) When reciting the blessing, "He Who clothes the naked," think about the great gift of garments

10) When reciting the words, "If I forget you, Jerusalem ..." sit on the floor and think of the loss of Yerushalayim.

---

* Renowned Torah personality (1908-2001) whose teachings and methods of attaining spiritual heights are studied the world over

GETTING HELP

SPIRITUAL THERAPY

Food is essential for the existence of all human life. We cannot subsist without food; it is vital for our ability to serve our Creator. However, food is not merely a corporeal entity. Our Sages observe that all food consists of a spiritual and a physical component. This is significant in understanding and treating the eating-disordered patient.

R' Eliyahu ben Shlomo Zalman, better known as the Vilna Gaon[1] notes that physical pleasure is markedly different from spiritual satisfaction. In the physical realm, the height of one's enjoyment is manifest in the anticipation of and participation in the pleasure. However, when we partake in spiritual enjoyment, our gratification is complete after we have concluded the exercise, that is, performing a *mitzvah* or learning Torah.

The Torah states *(Devarim 8:3),* "God afflicted you and let you hunger, then He fed you the *mahn*[2] ... in order to make you know that man does not live by bread alone, rather by everything that emanates from the mouth of God does man live."

The great sage Rabbi Aharon Kotler (1891-1962)[3] explains that the sustenance of man is not derived from the essence of the bread itself; rather, it is the directive of God that gives the bread the power and ability to sustain life, as it says *(ibid.) "al kol motza pi Hashem yichyeh ha'adam"* – by all that emanates from the mouth of God does man live. Thus, the food is permeated with spirituality derived from the word of Hashem. Moreover, the edict of God continually replenishes the food's capacity to sustain and satisfy man.

---

[1] One of the foremost leaders of world Jewry during the 18th century

[2] The heavenly bread that fell daily for the Jewish nation during their forty-year sojourn in the Sinai Desert

[3] Founder of the world-renowned Beth Medrash Govoha Talmudic Institute of Higher Learning, Lakewood, New Jersey

A similar correlation of the spiritual and physical aspect of food is highlighted by R' Chaim Volozhiner (1749-1821).[4] He cites the Kabbalist, R' Chaim Vital of the 16th century, who states that when a person does not eat for an extended period of time his weakened physical condition causes his soul to depart from his body. The question is: What sustenance does the spiritual soul derive from the physical food?

R' Volozhiner explains that the entire world was, in truth, created by the utterance of God. The heavens and earth, all of nature and vegetation, every creature was brought into being by the word of Hashem. Furthermore, the *Medrash* tells us that every blade of grass has a Heavenly guardian angel that commands it to grow. Thus, while the body may be sustained by the physical essence of the food, the soul derives its sustenance from the spiritual component — from the power of the One who causes it to exist.

Rabbi Yeshayah Horowitz,[5] cites the renowned Rabbi Eliyahu de Vidas,[6] who states that a unique spirit of holiness and purity envelops the individual who partakes of his food for the sake of Heaven, and his soul is nurtured. This is as it says in *Mishlei (13:25),* "A righteous person eats to satisfy his soul."

The Torah recounts that the Jewish nation grumbled about the blandness of the *mahn*; they pined for the fish and meat they had had in Egypt. In effect, they were complaining about a physical aspect of their life. Hashem addresses the issue by telling Moshe, "Gather for Me seventy men from the elders of Israel … and I will increase some of the spirit that is upon you and place it upon them." *(Bamidbar 11:16-17)*

What benefit or solution was there in His counsel to designate seventy spiritual giants for the formation of the Sanhedrin?[7]

---

[4] Preeminent disciple of the Vilna Gaon and author of the *Nefesh HaChaim*
[5] Known as the Shela HaKadosh, legendary rabbinical figure and mystic of the late 16th and early 17th century
[6] Early 16th century Kabbalist who wrote the *Sefer Reishis Chachmah*
[7] The ancient Jewish court system that consisted of 71 great Torah sages

Rav Samson Raphael Hirsch (1808-1888) explains that although the dissatisfaction of the people was expressed as a physical deficiency, it actually reflected a void in their spiritual well-being. Therefore, Hashem commanded Moshe to rescue them by imbuing them with some of his spirituality, that is, by giving them "spiritual food" so they would be content with the goodness of Hashem and they would not be overwhelmed with a feeling of physical deprivation.

Spiritual therapy is a course of therapy that addresses human behavior and physical health in the spiritual and religious realms. This regimen helps to address core issues and imbues patients with inspiration to fortify their inner connection with the Creator. By examining the problem through a spiritual prism, patients are empowered to develop the inner strength and spiritual awareness necessary to overcome obstacles along the road to recovery.

Spiritual therapy is a great healer of both body and soul. There is no doubt that the severe traumas that a person experiences can have an impact on the soul. In fact, we make due note in our daily morning prayers that Hashem guards and protects the soul within us, indicating that the soul – our life-giving essence – is always in need of protection from any kind of harm.[8] Oftentimes, however, the injury to the soul is overlooked, as concentration is focused on the trauma that the mind and body have endured. We must be mindful, however, that the soul — just as the mind and body — needs to heal.

> How is it that the Divine soul can influence the inner workings of the body? How are body and soul connected? R' Moshe Chaim Luzzato says, "The Divine soul directs the lower animal soul, and through it performs its necessary functions … The Divine soul is bound to the animal soul, and the animal soul is in turn linked to the most ethereal element of the blood."[9]

---

[8] "*Elokai Neshamah* – My God, the soul You placed within me is pure"
[9] *Derech Hashem*, III:1

It is interesting to note that our Sages tell us that every individual is infused with an "extra soul" on Shabbos and Yom Tov (Jewish holidays). The commentaries explain that the extra soul provides an added dimension of spirituality and expanded consciousness within each person, and also impacts on the body's delight in food and sleep on those days. Indeed, the soul and the body are inextricably bound together.

Rabbi Yaakov Leiner of Ishbitz (1828-1878) illustrates the unique bond that exists between the body and soul with the following verse:

The Prophet Yeshayah states *(26:9)*, "My soul yearns for You at night; as long as my spirit is within me I will seek You out."

Hashem Yisborach created man with a combination of body and soul that coexist in this world peacefully. There are times when one is subservient to the other, that is, the body is pained because of the soul or the soul is distressed because of the body. Nevertheless, they are intrinsically joined and they do not abandon each other.

At night, though, the soul of each person rises up to Hashem and testifies before the Heavenly Throne concerning what has transpired during the day, while the body remains asleep. It is this state to which Yeshayah refers. The body, in its isolation, yearns for its counterpart, which has ascended up high during the night.

Allegorically, the night is often used to describe the difficult periods during our lifetime when everything seems obscured and dismal. We tend to focus on the presenting needs of the body. In fact, though, explains the Ishbitzer, the physical body is actually thirsting for the soul during the darkness of the night.

This concept helps us understand the need for people suffering from an eating disorder to seek the proper treatment and effect their recovery in consonance with the yearning of the soul.

Spiritual counseling helps the individual to introspect; the self-evaluation which results is very enlightening. With this spiritual component, one is better able to understand and work through those areas of life that are wanting. Spiritual therapy establishes a connection to the source, our Creator. It links one's mind and heart to a higher power that provides a new level of self-empowerment, confidence and peace.

Healing and recovery can be facilitated through prayer, which is an outpouring of the soul. Faith in Hashem, seizing *mitzvah* opportunities, allowing ourselves to become infused with *simcha* (happiness) and song are also helpful means to effecting the healing process, as are participation and involvement in the celebration of the Shabbos and holidays.

A patient once remarked to me that one of the single greatest sources of encouragement for her was the knowledge that others were reciting a prayer specifically for her personal well-being.[10]

---

[10] This is known as the *Mi Shebeirach* prayer which is traditionally recited whenever the Torah is read in the synagogue. The prayer asks for divine intervention for a physical cure as well as spiritual healing for the ill individual, whose name is appropriately inserted, within the community of others who are facing illness.

Do's and Don'ts

If you are concerned that someone you know may have an eating disorder, here are helpful suggestions as to what you can do:

- Tell the person you want to help
- Express your concern
- Assure the person that they are not alone, and that you will try to help them in any way that you can
- Do not be judgmental or critical
- Try to get the person to seek professional help as soon as possible
- Try to learn as much as possible about eating disorders
- Avoid talking about food and weight
- Watch for signs of deteriorating physical or emotional health
- Be careful about personal prejudice or misconceptions about body image
- Do not comment on their weight or appearance
- Do not blame the individual, or allow yourself to get angry with them
- Do not become a pop-therapist
- Do not make mealtimes a battleground
- Do not try to make a person eat or insist that they gain weight
- Never compare the person to other individuals

Be very careful about what you say while in the company of a person suffering from an eating disorder. Remarks like the following can have a negative effect and further complicate his eating disorder.

Do not say:

- You look terrible
- I wish I had that problem
- I'll give you a few months to get over this illness
- What have you eaten today?
- I am happy to see how much you ate today

- Why can't you just sit down and eat like a normal person?
- Why are you so into yourself?
- You're ruining the family
- It may be your eating disorder, but you don't know how it's affecting me
- You're just doing this for attention
- No one will ever like you with your weight like this
- There's no use going for counseling; it will obviously never help you
- Be patient; recovery takes time.

FYI

Determining Your Ideal Weight

Male		Female	
Height	**Ideal Weight**	**Height**	**Ideal Weight**
4'6"	63-77 lbs.	4'6"	63-77 lbs.
4'7"	68-84 lbs.	4'7"	68-83 lbs.
4'8"	74-90 lbs.	4'8"	72-88 lbs.
4'9"	79-97 lbs.	4'9"	77-94 lbs.
4'10"	85-103 lbs.	4'10"	81-99 lbs.
4'11"	90-110 lbs.	4'11"	86-105 lbs.
5'0"	95-117 lbs.	5'0"	90-110 lbs.
5'1"	101-123 lbs.	5'1"	95-116 lbs.
5'2"	106-130 lbs.	5'2"	99-121 lbs.
5'3"	112-136 lbs.	5'3"	104-127 lbs.
5'4"	117-143 lbs.	5'4"	108-132 lbs.
5'5"	122-150 lbs.	5'5"	113-138 lbs.
5'6"	128-156 lbs.	5'6"	117-143 lbs.
5'7"	133-163 lbs.	5'7"	122-149 lbs.
5'8"	139-169 lbs.	5'8"	126-154 lbs.
5'9"	144-176 lbs.	5'9"	131-160 lbs.
5'10"	149-183 lbs.	5'10"	135-165 lbs.
5'11"	155-189 lbs.	5'11"	140-171 lbs.
6'0"	160-196 lbs.	6'0"	144-176 lbs.
6'1"	166-202 lbs.	6'1"	149-182 lbs.
6'2"	171-209 lbs.	6'2"	153-187 lbs.
6'3"	176-216 lbs.	6'3"	158-193 lbs.
6'4"	182-222 lbs.	6'4"	162-198 lbs.
6'5"	187-229 lbs.	6'5"	167-204 lbs.
6'6"	193-235 lbs.	6'6"	171-209 lbs.
6'7"	198-242 lbs.	6'7"	176-215 lbs.
6'8"	203-249 lbs.	6'8"	180-220 lbs.
6'9"	209-255 lbs.	6'9"	185-226 lbs.
6'10"	214-262 lbs.	6'10"	189-231 lbs.
6'11"	220-268 lbs.	6'11"	194-237 lbs.
7'0"	225-275 lbs.	7'0"	198-242 lbs.

Source: Rush University Medical Center, Chicago, IL

BODY MASS INDEX TABLE

BMI	19	20	21	22	23	24	25	26	27	28	29	30	31	32	33	34	35
Height (inches)	Body Weight (pounds)																
58	91	96	100	105	110	115	119	124	129	134	138	143	148	153	158	162	167
59	94	99	104	109	114	119	124	128	133	138	143	148	153	158	163	168	173
60	97	102	107	112	118	123	128	133	138	143	148	153	158	163	168	174	179
61	100	106	111	116	122	127	132	137	143	148	153	158	164	169	174	180	185
62	104	109	115	120	126	131	136	142	147	153	158	164	169	175	180	186	191
63	107	113	118	124	130	135	141	146	152	158	163	169	175	180	186	191	197
64	110	116	122	128	134	140	145	151	157	163	169	174	180	186	192	197	204
65	114	120	126	132	138	144	150	156	162	168	174	180	186	192	198	204	210
66	118	124	130	136	142	148	155	161	167	173	179	186	192	198	204	210	216
67	121	127	134	140	146	153	159	166	172	178	185	191	198	204	211	217	223
68	125	131	138	144	151	158	164	171	177	184	190	197	203	210	216	223	230
69	128	135	142	149	155	162	169	176	182	189	196	203	209	216	223	230	236
70	132	139	146	153	160	167	174	181	188	195	202	209	216	222	229	236	243
71	136	143	150	157	165	172	179	186	193	200	208	215	222	229	236	243	250
72	140	147	154	162	169	177	184	191	199	206	213	221	228	235	242	250	258
73	144	151	159	166	174	182	189	197	204	212	219	227	235	242	250	257	265
74	148	155	163	171	179	186	194	202	210	218	225	233	241	249	256	264	272
75	152	160	168	176	184	192	200	208	216	224	232	240	248	256	264	272	279
76	156	164	172	180	189	197	205	213	221	230	238	246	254	263	271	279	287

The body of every individual is composed of bone, muscle and fat which are included in the consideration of one's ideal weight. Calculating the Body Mass Index (BMI) provides a measure of the body fatness for most people and is based on height and weight (applicable to adults, both men and women).

BMI Categories:
- Underweight = <18.5
- Normal weight = 18.5-24.9
- Overweight = 25-29.9
- Obesity = BMI of 30 or greater

To use the table, find the appropriate height in the left-hand column labeled Height. Move across to a given weight (in pounds). The number at the top of the column is the BMI at that height and weight.

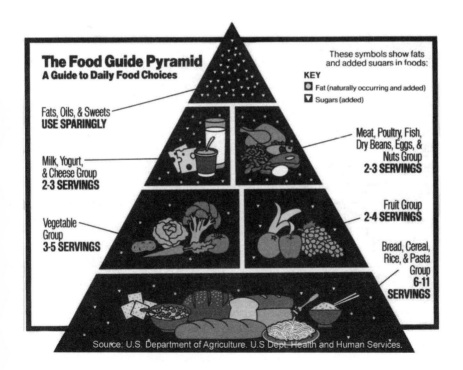

FOR CLINICAL USE

ESTHER'S STORY

It was a day in early March, but as I made my way to see a patient with an eating disorder at one of the facilities in the New York metropolitan area, it was snowing once again. I had been traveling there regularly throughout the winter, and looked forward to an easier drive the next time, during the Intermediary Days of *Pesach*.

As I drove, I wondered about the observant young woman Rosie kept mentioning was walking past the room during my visits with her. As she ambled by, Rosie said, she would glance into the room, apparently interested to note that I was there. She had never spoken to me, however.

On my next visit that *Pesach* holiday, the observant young woman approached me as I was headed to visit with Rosie. I nodded to her and said, *"A gut Yom Tov."* She seemed to be discomfited and ill at ease, but I sensed that she wanted to say something. She finally mustered up enough courage to softly say that she wanted to ask me a *sheiloh* (question of Jewish law).

Once we began to talk, it became obvious that Yiddish was her first language. She couldn't understand why she had to be confined to this facility. Moreover, the language barrier was making it difficult for her to understand the rules of the program. The cultural differences only served to further exacerbate the situation. She believed that the staff didn't like her because she was not like all the other patients on the floor. For example, she said, all the other patients would lounge around in comfortable pants or sweats, while she dressed in accordance with Jewish tradition.

I spoke to her quietly, trying to reassure her, and offered to speak to the staff on her behalf.

After a few moments of silence, she inquired, "You know my name is Esther?"

I said, "No, I didn't know. But now that you told me I know."

She then remarked, "I always wondered why my parents named me Esther. I figured it out here," she said. "Here I am *hester* [hidden] – everybody sees me, but they don't see me. Nobody knows me; they don't know who I am. I am concealed. I am asking for help, but they don't understand me. I am *hester* – I am obscured."

She began to cry softly, and then finally blurted out, "I will tell you the reason why I wanted to talk to you so much."

She explained that every day during *Pesach* she was given a slice of cheese to eat along with *matzah*, because that was the protocol of her diet. However, they didn't realize that she only eats special *shmurah matzah* [literally *matzah* that has been watched, that is, the process of making *matzos* is supervised from the time the wheat is harvested to ensure that no drop of moisture touches the wheat], and they were putting the cheese on regular machine made *matzos*. Although she knew that she had to eat the cheese, she was distressed because the cheese had touched the *matzah*. Before she actually ingested the cheese, she meticulously tried to remove all the *matzah* crumbs that adhered to the piece of cheese.

Her anguished question to me was: "How serious is the sin that I have committed?"

DISCERNING THE SENSITIVITIES OF THE OBSERVANT JEWISH PATIENT: DISTINGUISHING BETWEEN JEWISH RITUALS AND EATING-DISORDERED RITUALS

By Rabbi Dovid Goldwasser and Elizabeth Frenkel, PhD*

Within Jewish law, the *mitzvah* (good deed) of taking care of one-self and one's health is one of the most important undertakings that a person faces. This obligation is so important that, if necessary, almost any other law or custom can and should be temporarily overridden in order to perform this *mitzvah*. However, in the case of an observant Jew with an eating disorder, it can be difficult for them to acknowledge and act on this. Furthermore, a lack of education and awareness among the treatment community can make it difficult to accurately discern when a patient is correctly following the law and when the patient's eating disorder has twisted that person's perception of the law to suit its own purposes. The following is an attempt to lay out some of the most basic principles of Jewish observance, while not necessarily all-inclusive, as they relate to eating disorder treatment. These principles should help those in the treatment community better understand and serve this population.

Keeping Kosher: Following Jewish Dietary Laws

Kashrus, or Jewish dietary laws, like other areas of Jewish observance are determined through three levels of authority. *Torah* (the Jewish Holy Scriptures) states the explicit laws. The laws are then interpreted by the rabbis and this was codified in a series of books called the *Talmud*. These laws and their interpretations have been further expanded. There are complex customs that may vary across observant communities. For example, the Torah explicitly forbids cooking a kid in its mother's milk. The *Talmud*

---

* Dr. Frenkel is supervising psychologist of the Eating Disorders Program at the University Medical Center of Princeton.

prohibits cooking any meat and milk dishes together. The Code of Jewish Laws and the commentaries then prohibited cooking milk and meat dishes uncovered in the same oven or using the same utensils for both dairy and meat. Custom, in some communities but not others, also prohibits eating cheese and fish together. There are different levels of prohibition and pro-scription of activity, with the Torah being the highest authority.

The purpose of the dietary laws: It is important for treatment providers who work with the observant community to understand that the dietary laws are not just an arbitrary set of guidelines. Jewish laws are a standard of living to help the Jewish people live holy lives and to behave at all times in a manner worthy of God's presence in our lives. Therefore Jews may not mix milk and meat in any manner, that is, cooking, baking, serving, eating. Jews may not eat animals that are listed as "unclean" by the Torah or have not been slaughtered according to ritual law. And Jews may only eat animals that have been killed in a prescribed way that minimizes the animal's suf-fering. All these rules are designed to make Jews mindful of what they eat and to remind them that eating, like all other behavior, can and should be done in a holy manner.

What to eat and what not to eat: As mentioned above, observant Jews may not mix milk and meat at the same meal or on the same dishes or uten-sils. Under normal circumstances, an observant Jew must wait 20 minutes after eating dairy products before eating meat (or must rinse out their mouth). However, one must wait 6 hours after eating meat before con-suming dairy products. When a person's health is at risk, or for purposes of eating disordered treatment, it is deemed necessary to eat a particular food before the expiration of the waiting period, rabbinical authorities should be consulted.

In order to keep kosher, Jews may only eat certain meats and those meats are only kosher if they have been killed in the prescribed way by a trained butcher. For the purposes of *kashrus*, fish is not considered a meat since it can't be killed in a humane way, as it will die as a result of being removed from the water. Fish is therefore considered *parve*. Most dairy products, fruits, vegetables, grains, and water are inherently kosher; however there can be problems because of infestations of insects that are not kosher (particularly with strawberries, raspberries, broccoli, brussel sprouts, and lettuce).

Certification: In order for packaged foods to be kosher, they must be certified by an overseeing body. Each individual overseeing body has their own symbol. Both the process of certification and the symbols themselves are referred to as *hechsher*. There are many different overseeing bodies and some are more common, some are seen as more stringent, and others are highly specialized to a local community. In general, a K by itself on a packaged food is not a kosher certification that is accepted. There must be a symbol indicating the specific group, or sponsoring agency, that made the certification. In many observant communities, there are only certain symbols that are deemed acceptable. However, for the purpose of eating disorder treatment, patients should be able to eat food with any common *hechsher*. It may be necessary to consult with a religious mentor considering the permissibility of eating food with different *hechshers* while in treatment. (See Appendix A for a list of 10 of the most commonly accepted *hechshers*.)

Kosher cooking: Kosher households have separate sets of dishes, utensils, pots and pans for cooking and eating dairy and meat. They may even have separate ovens, sinks, dishwashers, or entirely separate kitchens. At the very least, they never have foods in them that are inherently not kosher. For treatment purposes, this level of observation may not be possible. If a treatment facility does not have a kosher kitchen and kosher dishes, then other steps can be taken to accommodate observant patients. Patients can eat on paper goods with plastic utensils. Kosher meals can be brought in from outside sources. These foods can be kept in the same refrigerator/freezer as non-kosher foods as long as none of the food is placed into the refrigerator/freezer while it is still very hot. The foods that are kosher must be wrapped and taped with a seal indicating that this is kosher food. Microwave ovens and standard ovens that have not been made kosher can be used as long as the kosher food being heated has been completely double wrapped. If necessary, ovens can be made kosher reasonably easily under the supervision of a knowledgeable observant Jew.

Many treatment programs may find it difficult to offer a range of kosher foods to observant patients. Depending on the facilities of the program and the applicable state and federal regulations, different options may be available. Some programs may be able to provide a kosher kitchen and prepare kosher meals on site. Other programs may only be able to provide hot kosher meals if they have been frozen. It may be desirable, in order to offer some variety to patients, to allow patients' families to bring in prepared foods from home, in order to provide a wider selection of meal options. Some communities call on observant people themselves to "light the fire" or start the cooking process by turning on the oven/stove.

Jewish Rituals in the Dining Room

In order to preserve the holiness of the food that is prepared, the food must be consumed in a way that upholds the sanctity of the meal. There are many rituals surrounding meals that should be understood by the treatment provider, in order to distinguish Jewish ritual from the eating disorder. These rituals include hand-washing, prayer, and eating foods in a prescribed order. In general, the rituals around food and eating are simple and relatively brief. If a behavior that the patient is engaging in is taking a particularly long time, it is questionable and an authority should be consulted.

Hand Washing: Jewish law prescribes hand washing upon waking in the morning, after any sleep of greater than 30 minutes, and before every meal. The ritual is to pour a cup of water over each hand between one and three times and to say a brief prayer. If the patient continues past three rinses, repeats the washing multiple times, or prays at length, then they are going beyond Jewish ritual and this can and should be addressed by the treatment team.

Prayer: Observant Jews must pray before and after eating. The prayer before eating is very brief and should take less than a minute. The prayer after the meal is longer if patients have eaten a minimum amount of bread. If this is the case, they need to recite five paragraphs. If not, the prayer is again very short.

The order of the meal: There are many Jewish rituals that may be observed while eating, some of which are more common than others. The most common is the order in which certain foods are to be eaten. Dairy must be eaten before meat, with time left in between. Fish should also be eaten before meat and the patient must drink something in between. On the Sabbath and other holidays, there are certain foods that must be blessed and eaten in a particular order. First, candles are lit and a blessing is said. Then there is a prayer over wine or grape juice, hand washing, and a blessing over bread. Then the meal proceeds from fish to meat to dessert. For the patient in a treatment facility there is some flexibility concerning this.

Other rituals may involve cutting bread or other foods or chewing in a particular way, as described in rabbinic law. If you have questions as to the legitimacy of a patient's statement that certain rituals are religiously mandated, it is best to consult a rabbi to confirm this. The rabbi will likely be able to reassure the patient as to what rituals may be suspended to promote the patient's healthy recovery.

Observing the Holy Days

The most important Jewish holiday is the Sabbath. There are many other holy days, some of which will be familiar to the average American and many of which will not. Many Americans will have heard of the High Holidays (*Rosh Hashanah* and *Yom Kippur*), Chanukah and Passover. They may not have heard of *Sukkos, Purim, Shavuos, Tisha B'Av,* and many others. They might have misperceptions of the relative importance of those holidays and may not fully understand the rituals that go with them. The following is a brief discussion of the holidays[1] and how they impact or are impacted by treatment.

---

[1] Jewish time differs from secular time in two important ways. First, the day begins at sundown. Therefore, holidays start and end at sundown. Second, the Jewish calendar is a lunar calendar. Therefore, the holidays do not fall on the same date on the Julian calendar from year to year.

"Work" and the holidays: Jews are forbidden from "working" on the Sabbath and many of the holidays, but there is a different meaning to "work" under these circumstances than merely performing a paying job. Jews are forbidden from doing anything that creates something else on the Sabbath since this is the day God finished creation and rested. Jews are literally commanded to rest on the Sabbath and not engage in any of the 39 "acts of labor" as delineated in the Talmud. To the observant patient, this means, for example, no direct use of electricity and no writing. In an inpatient or residential setting, the patient may need to leave certain lights on in their room for the entire Sabbath or may need to be excused from writing. Observant Jews may ride in a special Shabbos automatic elevator when necessary where they do not need to push the buttons to create the electrical command for the elevator to move, but many will prefer to take the stairs. These patients may need tissues or pre-torn tissues for the restrooms prepared before the Sabbath. Observant patients in day programs may need permission to leave early on Friday to get home before the Sabbath begins, particularly in the wintertime when days are short.

Fast days: There are two major fasts (*Yom Kippur* and *Tisha B'Av*) and five minor fasts throughout the Jewish year. The major fasts are observed from sunset to sunset and the minor fasts are observed from sunrise to sunset, although it is permitted to get up before sunrise to eat breakfast. Pregnant and nursing women may be excused from the fast, and young children do not fast. Any person whose life and health would be endangered by fasting is forbidden to fast. Even if a patient is currently in good health but fasting might trigger dangerous behaviors, fasting is forbidden. However, observant Jews may find it extremely difficult to accept this prohibition, especially if they have an eating disorder and are ambivalent about their recovery.

It is important to find out ahead of time when an observant patient would normally observe fasts and come up with a healthy eating plan. This will likely involve consultation with a rabbi and a physician, if there is not a physician already on the patient's eating disorder treatment team. Jewish law states that if a doctor says that a person must eat on a fast day, that person must eat and if a doctor says it is permissible to fast and a person believes that it would be unhealthy for him to fast, that person must eat. It is crucial to rule on the side of caution in order to observe the *mitzvah* of self-care. However, there are ways to work with eating-disordered individuals to be sensitive to their feelings about breaking the fast. One way to help patients with this dilemma is to encourage them to pray to God for acceptance of this need. (See "Prayers Related to Recovery".) On *Yom Kippur*, for people who are not in a program, eating and drinking small amounts at intervals all day long in order to meet their nutritional needs may be permissible. This is considered under Torah law to meet the conditions of the fast. Other solutions may be agreed on by the treatment team and the patient with rabbinic guidance.

Passover: Of all the Jewish holidays, Passover has the most extensive rules about the preparation and consumption of food. In order to recall the flight from Egypt in biblical times and God's redemption of the Jews from slavery, Jews are forbidden from eating anything leavened. This is because the Jews had to leave Egypt so fast that they did not have time to allow their bread to rise, but instead made flat cakes now called *matzah*. Jews may not eat products made with grains unless they have followed strict guidelines and many Jews will also not eat foods made with other common bases for bread (such as corn). There are extensive Torah and rabbinic laws and customs about removing bread and forbidden foods from the home, cleaning the home, and preparing the ceremonial meal (called the *seder*). Furthermore, many Jews who would not otherwise consider themselves observant do attend Seders and observe the dietary guidelines of Passover. As usual with Jewish law, if necessary, the strict adherence to these prohibitions should be discussed with an authority on Jewish law. However, it may be possible for the patient to work with her team to develop an appropriate meal plan that would allow her to follow the Passover guidelines, especially if she is allowed to bring in food from home for the duration of the holiday.

The Passover *seder* is a ceremonial meal in which the story of the Jews' exodus from Egypt is retold in a specified order. Participants are required to eat certain foods for their symbolism related to the holiday, for example, wine, *matzoh,* and a large holiday meal is shared. The *seder* can be very difficult for patients because of the focus on food and because of the expectation to eat a large meal, often in the presence of extended family and/or members of the community. It can also be difficult for patients to maintain a healthy mind-set regarding food inclusion while observing traditions that focus on food restriction. It is very important to address issues surrounding attendance at the *seder* and the observation of the restrictions on eating only Passover products with any Jewish patients who observe Passover – not just the observant patients. As always, it may be desirable to involve the patient's rabbi in discussions of the most appropriate way for the patient to observe the holiday, given his current health and his progress in recovery.

There are several other Jewish holidays throughout the year, all of which include several large meals with family and friends. Many holidays are known for a specific food item. For example on *Shavuos*, Jews eat dairy products, and on *Purim*, Jews eat *hamantaschen*, a type of dough cookie with a filling. The patient may need to discuss these experiences in therapy.

Decorum in Jewish Behavior

Observant Jews follow a code of behavior that has developed both through law and custom to enhance Jews' awareness of God's constant presence in their lives and to behave in a way that is respectful and worthy of that presence. Some of these standards are easily observable to others, such as codes of dress. Others are less obvious, such as the prohibition against speaking ill of others. Many of these standards might impact a patient's treatment and should be discussed.

Rules regarding the opposite gender: Observant Jews will not touch a member of the opposite gender who is not an immediate family member. Spouses will often not touch each other in public. Observant Jews usually would not allow themselves to be alone in a room with a member of the opposite gender who is not a first-degree relative. Physical contact is allowed for professional reasons, such as treatment by a doctor. However, treatment providers need to be aware of and sensitive to their patients' concerns about these issues. Treatment providers working with the observant community should be careful not to touch observant patients unless it is strictly necessary for medical reasons. So, for example, it is acceptable for a doctor to touch a patient if it is necessary to conduct a physical exam but the doctor should not hug an observant patient, pat them on the arm or back, or give them a "high five." In general, one should not initiate any physical contact, even a handshake, with a member of the opposite gender.

Modesty: Observant Jews are expected to behave with modesty and humility at all times. This modesty is reflected in the way observant Jews dress and the subjects about which they speak. Observant Jews are expected to wear modest clothing. Women are generally expected to wear clothing that covers their elbows and knees; often the standard is even more modest. In many communities, women are expected to always wear skirts. Married women must cover their hair. Observant men may or may not consider it appropriate to wear short sleeves. More casual clothing may be allowed at home in some communities. If that is the case, there might be different expectations between parents and children regarding the standard for dress while a patient is in a hospital. Observant patients may feel it is immodest to speak in group, to eat in front of others, or to address issues that might be seen as reflecting poorly on someone else.

Observant families, many of whom do not have much exposure to the media, often have serious concerns about the interaction of their family members with the secular community. They worry that the patient will be exposed to immodest dress and inappropriate topics of conversation both in group and in the treatment community. It is important to address these concerns with families of observant patients. While shielding the observant patient completely from exposure to the secular culture may be difficult, it is often possible to reassure these families by developing a reasonable treatment plan that minimizes exposure of children to unacceptable activities.

Tikkun Olam: Repairing the World

In Judaism, there is great importance put on the *mitzvah* of repairing the world. This concept should resonate with those who have chosen to work in the helping professions. In creating a safe treatment environment for members of the observant community, we collaborate with our patients and their families to repair the world one person at a time.

Appendix A: Ten Commonly Accepted Kosher Certifications*

ARK

Badatz

CRC – Chicago and Brooklyn

(Hisachdus Harrabanim)

KAJ

National Kashrut

OK

OU

Star-K

* There are additional certifications which are also reliable. We have only presented a sample of some of the renowned certifications.

Appendix B: Listing Of Jewish Holidays

Rosh Hashanah is the Jewish New Year, also known as the Day of Judgment.

The **Fast of Gedaliah** commemorates the assassination of Gedaliah Ben Achikam, the governor of Israel, and marks the final exile of the Jews remaining in Israel after the destruction of the Temple.

Yom Kippur, the holiest day of the Jewish year, is a 25-hour fast that begins at sunset the evening before and ends after nightfall on the day of Yom Kippur.

Succos is a seven-day holiday commemorating the forty-year period during which the Jewish nation wandered in the desert and dwelt in temporary shelters.

Shemini Atzeres is celebrated on the eighth day of Succos and marks the closure of the holiday of Succos.

Simchas Torah immediately follows the day of Shemini Atzeres and celebrates the completion and beginning of the weekly "Reading of the Torah."

Chanukah, an eight-day holiday, commemorates the historic defeat of the Greek army by the small group of Maccabees and the subsequent miracle of the oil in the Temple.

Asarah B'Teves is a fast day marking the beginning of the destruction of the Temple. On this day in history, Nevuchadnezzar laid siege to Jerusalem.

Tu B'Shvat is the New Year for Trees, and it is marked by eating the fruit for which Israel is praised in the Torah, i.e., grapes, figs, pomegranates, olives and dates.

Taanis Esther precedes the day of Purim and commemorates the three-day fast that Esther requested of the Jews to avert Haman's evil decree against them.

Purim is a day of joy and celebration commemorating the time when the Jews of Persia were saved from extermination.

Shushan Purim, which is actually observed as Purim itself in walled cities like Jerusalem, has become an additional day of joy and celebration also in those places where it is not observed as the actual day of Purim.

Pesach (Passover) is an eight-day holiday commemorating the exile of the enslaved Jews from Egypt.

Pesach Sheini was a day of rejoicing for those who had been able to bring the sacrifices on the holiday of Passover itself. Some people have a custom to eat leftover *matzoh* to commemorate the offering that was eaten with *matzoh*.

Lag B'Omer is observed as a day of rejoicing. It marks the day when the plague that killed the students of Rabbi Akiva stopped.

Shavuos is a two-day holiday commemorating the day the Torah was given by God to the Jewish people on Mount Sinai.

Shiva Asar B'Tammuz is a fast day commemorating the day the walls of Jerusalem were breached, allowing the invading armies to enter the city.

Tisha B'Av is a twenty-five hour fast day commemorating the destruction of the Holy Temple.

HOPE AND RECOVERY

SHIRA'S STORY

Today is a special day! I received an invitation in the mail, inviting me to the wedding of a young lady whom I first met when she was severely anorexic and had been hospitalized on several occasions.

Over the years that I met with her in counseling, there were times when she was literally ready to give up. Shira once told me, "I've lost my grip on things … being in Ana's [anorexia's] clutches is too torturous. Maybe the other world wouldn't be so bad."

In the beginning, Shira could only come with her parents when she was well enough to travel. Her parents would sit outside my office reciting *Tehillim* while she met with me. It was especially heartbreaking to hear Shira blaming herself for being ill. Upon exiting the office, she would invariably burst out in tears, crying to her parents, "Please forgive me. I am sorry to cause you so much distress. At least you have *nachas* from your other children." Week after week, I would listen and see this scene replayed.

Shira's teachers, apprised of her situation, would call because they were afraid they might say something inappropriate to her. One of her teachers told me, ""Shira is probably one of the best students I have ever had. It's very difficult to see her now in this condition."

Fortunately, Shira – with much *siyata d'shmaya* (Divine Assistance)— never completely lost her motivation to go on. Despite numerous failures and setbacks, she made every effort to work on the suggested program for her recovery. Spurred on by her indomitable spirit, she doggedly persisted in her determination to recover.

The turning point came when Shira's cousin arrived from Israel for a prolonged visit. Growing up poor and deprived, Shira's cousin was in need of much tender loving emotional and physical care. Shira, who was inherently good-hearted and an extremely capable young lady, immediately assumed full responsibility for her cousin. Strangely enough, the more that Shira lent a hand to her cousin, the more she helped herself.

Slowly, Shira turned the corner. Little by little, there were improvements in Shira's condition. Changes came in small baby steps. They were subtle at first, but became more noticeable as time went on. After a while, Shira was able to discontinue her weekly visits and come less frequently.

Since she had been doing well on her own, I hadn't heard from Shira in about a year. Until today, when I opened her beautiful invitation, with a personal handwritten note thanking me for everything and inviting me to give her a *bracha* under the *chuppah*. She wanted me to give her one more *bracha* for a lifetime, similar to the blessings that I gave her every week.

FAITH AND COURAGE

To be sure recovery is a slow and steady process. The Talmud tells us *(Yuma 80a)*, *"Tafasta merubah lo tafasta…* — When you try to take a large amount you will not take anything. If you try to take a small amount, you will be successful."

People often think that they will be able to "cure" anorexia or bulimia in a few days, a few visits or – at most — in a few weeks. It doesn't happen that way. There is no way to rush the time it takes to implement the necessary changes that need to take place. It requires much patience as well as the realization and understanding that the only progress that is true and long-lasting is that which consists of small "baby steps."

King David tells us in *Tehillim (27:14)*, "Hope to Hashem, strengthen yourself and He will give you courage, and hope to Hashem."

Our commentaries question the need to repeat the phrase "hope to Hashem." They explain that this is meant to discourage the person from succumbing to despair. If one anticipated deliverance and it was not forth-coming, the individual should not despair. One should immediately for-tify himself with renewed hope and restored faith.

"Heal us, Hashem, then we will be healed; save us – then we will be saved, for You are our praise. Bring complete recovery for all our ailments, for You are God, King, the faithful and compassionate Healer ..." (Morning Prayers)

Rabbi Yecheskel Abramsky, eminent Torah sage of the 20th century (1886-1976), asks: Why do we include the phrase "for You are our praise," only in this particular prayer for healing and not in any other prayer?

Rabbi Abramsky explains that when a person is healed he could mistakenly attribute his recovery to the physician. In this *tefillah* we affirm that one's restoration to health comes directly from Hashem. The doctor is only His messenger. "You, Hashem, deserve the praise, and for that we indeed praise, You, Hashem."

Many people with eating disorders who are treated early and appropriately can achieve a full and long-term recovery. Treatment must be personalized for the individual patient, and most treatment plans will include therapy, (e.g. counseling or cognitive-behavioral therapy), a nutritional program, and sometimes medication.

The first and most important step toward recovery is the eating-disordered individual's admission that he needs help and his willingness to accept it. Since people with eating disorders often are unwilling to admit that they are ill and resist getting treatment, it is extremely helpful to have a family member or a devoted friend who can facilitate this phase. Notwithstanding the various interventions, complete recovery is ultimately the responsibility of the patient.

An eating disorder isn't about food. It is usually symptomatic of intense and personal issues that must be addressed, and therefore recovery is not limited to education about healthy eating or achieving a normal weight.

There are a variety of different treatment options, but it is important to determine which approach is most suitable for the individual patient.

At the time of diagnosis, it must be determined whether the eating disorder patient is in immediate danger and must be hospitalized to stabilize the situation. This would be indicated, for example, if there were excessive and/or rapid weight loss or severe metabolic disturbances.

Eating disorders are complex and for the patient suffering from an ED, healing is more complex than simply following some guidelines. However, it is helpful to become familiar with and develop an awareness of different courses of action and strategies that are usually implemented to facilitate the patient's healing process. What is most important at all times is that patients feel that they are in a comfortable and safe environment that is conducive to their recovery with effective counseling.

Part of recovery is based on connecting with self, family, and the community. Community service – volunteer work or work that helps others – enables the eating disordered patient to look beyond himself, to develop new interests and hobbies that redirect his focus on food. As a result, his self-perception improves and his self-worth and purpose in life are more positively impacted.

Another component of recovery emphasizes the development of the patient's connection to his spirituality. The patient learns to integrate his faith to promote his emotional and behavioral well-being.

Rabbi Pinchas HaLevi Horowitz (1731-1805) posits that the action of eating encompasses two realms. There is the desire of man to sate his physical hunger, but there is also a second sphere in which the consumption of food involves a spiritual factor.

As we know, there are four levels of creation in the world: *domem* – the inanimate object; *tzomei'ach* – vegetation; *chai* – living creatures, that is, animals; and *medaber* – the human being who possesses the power of speech.

Rabbi Horowitz explains that one aspect of *tikkun ha'olam* – repairing the world – involves the elevation of each creation to a higher plane. Thus, when a person partakes of his food with a divine purpose, he raises that food to a higher level by imbuing it with a spiritual element. In this way, the *tzomei'ach* – vegetation – is raised to the level of a *chai,* so to speak, and achieves its higher root in the world.

Shlomo HaMelech writes *(Koheles 3:21),* "Who perceives that the spirit of man is the one that ascends on high, while the spirit of the beast is the one that descends down into the earth."

The focus of man's intent impacts on the significance of his meal. If man's thoughts are committed to fulfilling his physical desire, then the food retains its banality. However, if man adds a spiritual dimension to his eating – as stated in *Mishlei (13:25),* "A righteous person eats to satisfy his soul" — then the food is exalted to the next level.

The Mareh Bazak offers another interesting insight into the concept of food. He suggests that just as Hashem provided man with food to satiate his physical hunger, He also intended to have that food satisfy man's soul, by directing us to fulfill the many *mitzvos* associated with that which we eat.

For example, when one works in the field to plant wheat for bread, the Torah specifies numerous *mitzvos:* One is forbidden to hybridize certain species of seeds when planting *(kilayim).* When one plows the earth, he cannot yoke the ox and donkey together. One may not muzzle his ox while it is threshing, which would prevent it from eating any wheat. During harvest, there are various *mitzvos* with regard to the welfare of the poor. One is commanded to leave the edge of his field for them; to allow the poor to collect the stalks that have fallen to the ground; and not to retrieve a sheaf that was forgotten in the field. There are also specific gifts that are reserved for the *kohen (terumos* and *maasros)* and tithes for the *levi.*

Once the grain has been ground into flour, and the bread is being made, one has the *mitzvah* of *challah.* Before we partake of the bread, we wash and then recite the proper blessings.

Thus, not only is the body gratified when it eats the food, but the *nefesh,* the soul, has already been sated with a huge number of *mitzvos* involved in the preparation of the food.

There is no doubt that every individual has the ability to regain his health and recover. The important point to remember is that the ED is, in reality, an unhealthy coping mechanism that co-exists with a psychological weakness. Therefore:

- The patient must explore and discover the causal feelings and issues underlying her eating disorder. For example, self-esteem issues, a drive for perfectionism, phobias, or dysfunctional relationships that evoke negative thoughts and emotions must be identified and expressed.
- It is essential for the patient to find new coping skills to replace his/her harmful food behaviors.
- The patient must develop a healthy support network to facilitate her recovery, such as a close friend, a family member, therapist, or support group.
- The patient must realize and appreciate his own uniqueness and importance, without regard to appearance, achievement or commendation.

Finally, the patient and her family must understand that the healing process is a slow and long journey that involves extensive work. Recovery is not driven solely by willpower; it involves changes in one's thought processes, emotions, and behaviors.

Starving Souls is dedicated to providing resources and support to those struggling with challenges in the areas of healthy eating and body image. A hotline has been established to answer the calls of people affected by an ED, or their parents/siblings. Appointments can be made for private counseling sessions.

Contact information for Rabbi Dovid Goldwasser:

718-677-3712 or starvingsouls@gmx.com

PRAYERS RELATED TO RECOVERY

בקשה

רבּוֹנוֹ שֶׁל עוֹלָם יְצַרְתָּנוּ גוּף וּנְשָׁמָה וְזֶה בְּלִי
זֶה אִי אֶפְשָׁר, וּכְשֵׁם שֶׁהַנְּשָׁמָה צְרִיכָה
מָזוֹן שֶׁל תּוֹרָה וּמִצְווֹת כַּךְ הַגּוּף צָרִיךְ מְזוֹנָהּ,
אַךְ כָּתַבְתָּ בְּתוֹרָתֶךָ וְנִשְׁמַרְתֶּם מְאֹד לְנַפְשֹׁתֵיכֶם
וּפֵירְשׁוּ חֲכָמֵינוּ זִכְרוֹנָם לִבְרָכָה. שֶׁרוֹב חוֹלִים
בָּאִים מֵאֲכִילָה, וְלָכֵן יְהִי רָצוֹן מִלְּפָנֶיךָ שֶׁתַּדְרִיכֵנוּ
בַּעֲבוֹדָתֶךָ, לְעָבְדְּךָ בְּאַהֲבָה וּבְיִרְאָה וּשְׂמְחָה
וְטוּב לֵבָב, עִם שִׂמְחַת הַחַיִּים אֲמִיתִי וְתִתְּנֵנִי
לְחֵן וּלְחֶסֶד וּלְרַחֲמִים בְּעֵינֶיךָ וּבְעֵינֵי כָּל רוֹאִי
וְאַל תְּבִיאֵנִי לֹא לִידֵי נִסָּיוֹן וְלֹא לִידֵי בִזָּיוֹן, וְזַכֵּנִי
שֶׁלֹּא אֶדָּמֶה לִרְאוֹת מַה שֶׁאֵינוֹ לְפִי הָאֱמֶת,
וְתֶן בִּי כֹּחַ וּבְרִיאוּת וִיכוֹלֶת מַסְפִּיק לַעֲבוֹר כָּל
הַנִּסְיוֹנוֹת, וְאַמְּצֵנוּ בְּאֵבָרֵי וְחַזְּקֵינוּ בְּגִידֵי וְתִסְמָכֵנוּ
בְּגוּפִי שֶׁלֹּא תְּאָרַע לִי שׁוּם כְּאֵב וְצַעַר וּפֶגַע רַע
וְחוֹלִי וּמֵיחוּשׁ, וְאֶהְיֶה בָּרִיא בַּעֲבוֹדָתֶךָ, וְתֶן
בְּלִבִּי לִרְאוֹת הָאוֹר וְהַטוֹב בְּכָל דָּבָר, וַאֲפִילוּ
דָּבָר שֶׁנִּרְאָה רַע בְּיוֹתֵר וּשֶׁאֶהְיֶה שָׁקֵט וְרַעֲנָן
תָּמִיד אָמֵן.

PRAYER FOR SERENTIY AND WELL-BEING

Master of the Universe, You created us body and soul — neither can exist without the other. Just as the soul requires Torah and good deeds for sustenance, so too the body requires its sustenance.

It is written in Your Torah, "And you shall safeguard your souls exceedingly." Our great sages, of blessed memory, explain that most sicknesses derive from food.

Therefore, may it be Your will to guide me in Your service, to be able to serve You with love and with awe, with happiness and contentment, and with true happiness in life. Grant me grace, kindness and mercy in Your eyes and in the eyes of all mankind.

I pray that I should not have to face situations of challenge or shame. May I merit to see myself for who I am, in my true goodness. Give me the strength, the health, and the ability to overcome all difficulties in my life. Empower me and strengthen my being; support me that no infirmities, pain, grief, mishaps or sickness should occur and I should be healthy to serve You.

Help my heart to see the light and the good in myself and in every situation, even at the darkest and most challenging times — and may I always be calm and tranquil. Amen.

תפלה למי שצריך לאכול ביום כיפור

רִבּוֹנוֹ שֶׁל עוֹלָם, מֶלֶךְ עֶלְיוֹן וְנוֹרָא, נָתַתָּ לָנוּ יוֹם קָדוֹשׁ נִפְלָא בִּקְדֻשָּׁתוֹ, וְהוּא קֹדֶשׁ קָדָשִׁים לִמְחִילָה וְלִכַפָּרָה, וְיוֹם הַכִּפּוּרִים שְׁמוֹ אֲשֶׁר בּוֹ כָּל הַיְצוּר כֻּלּוֹ חָל וְזָע מֵאֵימַת דִּינֶךָ וְעַמְּךָ בֵּית יִשְׂרָאֵל בָּנֶיךָ אֲהוּבֶיךָ נוֹשְׂאִים לְךָ תְּפִילָה כְּדֵי שֶׁתִּמְחוֹל לָהֶם וְיֵצְאוּ זַכָּאִים בְּדִינָם וּנְקִיִּים מִכָּל רְכֶב. וְאַתָּה בְּרֹב רַחֲמֶיךָ צִיוִּיתָנוּ לְהִתְעַנּוֹת מֵעֶרֶב עַד עֶרֶב כְּדֵי שֶׁנִּטַּהֵר לְפָנֶיךָ וְנָשׁוּב אֵלֶיךָ בְּלֵבָב שָׁלֵם. גַּם אֲנִי בִּנְךָ\בִּתְּךָ רוֹצֶה לְהִתְעַנּוֹת כְּדֵי לְקַיֵּם אֵת אֲשֶׁר צִיוִּיתָנוּ "וְעִנִּיתֶם אֵת נַפְשׁוֹתֵיכֶם".

אָב הָרַחֲמָן אַתָּה יְצַרְתַּנִי וְנָפַחְתָּ בִּי נְשָׁמָה טְהוֹרָה בִּכְדֵי שֶׁאוּכַל לְמַלֵּא אֵת יְעוּדִי בָּעוֹלָם הַשְּׁמִי זֶה. גָּלוּי וְיָדוּעַ לְפָנֶיךָ, יוֹצֵר הַכֹּל, כִּי אֲנִי כְּחֹמֶר בְּיַד הַיּוֹצֵר בִּרְצוֹתוֹ מַרְחִיב וּבִרְצוֹתוֹ מְקַצֵּר, וּמַחֲמַת חָלְיִי נִבְצַר מִמֶּנִּי בְּשָׁנָה זוֹ לָצוּם בְּיוֹם הֶעָשׂוֹרִי בְּתִשְׁרֵי, וְאִם אָצוּם יַזִּיק הַדָּבָר מְאֹד, חָלִילָה, לִבְרִיאוּתִי. בְּדַרְכֵּי אֲשֶׁר לֹא אוּכַל לְהַמְשִׁיךְ וְלַעֲבוֹד אוֹתְךָ וּלְקַיֵּם יוֹתֵר אֵת מִצְווֹתֶיךָ אֲשֶׁר הִנְחַלְתָּ לָנוּ בְּאַהֲבָתְךָ אוֹתָנוּ.

אָב הָרַחֲמָן. בְּלֵב כָּבֵד שָׁאַלְתִּי מוֹרֵי הוֹרָאָה וְהֵמָּה צִוּוּנִי אֲשֶׁר בְּטוֹבְלָה הִיא הִיא קַיּוּמָהּ - וְאִם בְּמַצָּבֵי הָרְפוּאִי הַיּוֹם אוֹכַל - אֶעֱשֶׂה אֵת רְצוֹנֶךָ. וּמִכֵּיוָן שֶׁשְּׁלוּחֶיךָ הִתִּירוּ לִי לֶאֱכוֹל בְּיוֹם קָדוֹשׁ זֶה, נָא קַבֵּל אֵת אֲכִילָתִי כְּקָרְבָּן עוֹלָה. וְכַאֲשֶׁר אֹכַל בְּשָׁנָה זוֹ תַּחְשֹׁב לִי כְּאִלּוּ צַמְתִּי אֵת כָּל הַצוֹם כֻּלּוֹ. וְכָל פֵּרוּר וּפֵרוּר שֶׁאֶכְנַס לְפִי יְהֵא בְּשִׂמְחָה וּבְכַוָּנָה גְּמוּרָה לְקַיֵּם מִצְווֹתֶיךָ וּלְהַאֲמִין בֶּאֱמוּנָה שְׁלֵמָה ש"כָּל מַה דְּעָבִיד רַחֲמָנָא לְטָב עָבִיד" וּבְוַדַּאי וּבְוַדַּאי שֶׁרְצוֹנְךָ הוּא אַךְ לְהֵטִיב לִי כָּל הַיָּמִים.

וְעוֹד אָב הָרַחֲמָן אָנָּא! מִתְחַנֵּן\מִתְחַנֶּנֶת אֲנִי אֵלֶיךָ, בְּרֹב רַחֲמֶיךָ שְׁלַח רְפוּאָה שְׁלֵמָה לְכָל אֵבֶר מֵאֵבָרַי, הָפֵחַ כֹּחַ וְחַיּוּת לְגוּפִי וּלְנַפְשִׁי בִּכְדֵי שֶׁאוּכַל לַעֲבוֹד אוֹתְךָ כָּל יְמֵי חֶלְדִּי וּלְפַרְסֵם אֵת יִחוּדְךָ וְאֵת שִׁמְךָ הַגָּדוֹל וְהַנּוֹרָא בְּכָל הָעוֹלָם כֻּלּוֹ, וְאֶזְכֶּה לַאֲרִיכוּת יָמִים וְשָׁנִים מִתּוֹךְ בְּרִיאוּת אֵיתָנָה. יְהִי רָצוֹן שֶׁלֹּא אֵבוֹשׁ בָּעוֹלָם הַזֶּה וְלֹא אֶכָּלֵם לָעוֹלָם הַבָּא כִּי הֲלֹא אֵת מִצְווֹתֶיךָ אֲנִי מְקַיֵּם\יָּמֵת. וּבִזְכוּת אֲכִילָה זוֹ שֶׁנֶּאֱכֶלֶת בִּקְדֻשָּׁה בַּיּוֹם הַקָּדוֹשׁ בְּיוֹתֵר לְעַמְּךָ יִשְׂרָאֵל שֶׁשְּׁלוּחֵי דְרַבָּנָן הִתִּירוּהָ, נִזְכֶּה לִגְאֻלָּה שְׁלֵמָה וּלְקַיֵּם מִצְווֹתֶיךָ מֵאַהֲבָה, אָמֵן סֶלָה.

249

Prayer For Those Who Need To Eat On Yom Kippur

Master of the Universe,
Supreme and Mighty King,
You gave us a holy day that is
wondrous in its holiness
For atonement and forgiveness
And its name is Yom Kippur.

On this day, the entire creation stands
before You in the awe of judgment.
And Your nation, the beloved people of Israel,
prays to You so that You may forgive them
And they may emerge righteous in judgment
and clear of any sin.
And You, in Your great mercy,
have commanded us to fast from eve to eve
So that we will be innocent before You,
And so that we return to You with all our hearts.

I, too, Your son/daughter wish to fast
So that I can fulfill that which You have commanded
"And your souls shall want."

Merciful Father, You created me,
You breathed into me a pure soul,
So that I might fulfill my purpose in this physical world.
It is revealed and known before You, Creator of all things,
That I am but clay in the Hands of the Creator.
Due to my illness, I am unable to fast this year
on the tenth of Tishrei
And if I were to fast, it would harm my health so that
I would be unable to continue to serve You
And to perform the commandments
That You have given us with Your great love.

cont.

PRAYER FOR THOSE WHO NEED TO EAT ON YOM KIPPUR *cont.*

Merciful Father, with a heavy heart,
I asked the spiritual mentors
And they have directed me
That my annulment of this commandment
is my fulfilling of it --
That if my health requires that I eat today,
I will thus fulfill Your will.
And since Your messengers allowed me to eat
on this holy day,
I ask You, please accept my eating
as part of my service to You.
And, when I will eat this year,
May it be considered as though I fasted the entire day.
May every morsel that I bring into my mouth be with great joy
And with the intention to fulfill Your will
And to believe with complete belief
That everything that G-d brings about is all for the good.
And more, merciful Father, please!
I pray to You, with Your great mercy
Please send me a complete recovery.
Breathe strength and life into my body and soul,
So that I can serve You all the days of my life,
And so that I may make known Your Oneness
And the greatness of Your awesome Name
in this entire world
And that I may merit length of days and years
in good health.
May it be Your will that I not be shamed
In this world and in the world to come.
In the merit of this food that I am eating in holiness
on this holiest of days,
May we merit the ultimate redemption
And the fulfillment of Your commandments with love,
Amein.

תפלה לבריאות
(מהרב חיד"א זצ"ל)

רִבּוֹנוֹ שֶׁל עוֹלָם, בְּרַחֲמֶיךָ תֵּן בָּנוּ כֹּחַ וּבְרִיאוּת וִיכֹלֶת מַסְפִּיק, וְחוֹזֶק וְאֹמֶץ בְּאֵבָרֵינוּ וְגִדֵינוּ וְנוּפֵינוּ לַעֲמוֹד עַל הַמִּשְׁמָר, וְלֹא יֶאֱרַע לָנוּ שׁוּם מִחוּשׁ וְשׁוּם כְּאֵב, וְנִהְיֶה שְׂמֵחִים וְטוֹבִים וּבְרִיאִים לַעֲבוֹדָתֶךָ. וְתַצִּילֵנוּ מִכָּל רָע, וְתַאֲרִיךְ יָמֵינוּ בְּטוֹב וּשְׁנוֹתֵינוּ בַּנְּעִימִים, וּמַלֵּא שְׁנוֹתֵינוּ, אוֹרֶךְ יָמִים וּשְׁנוֹת חַיִּים תּוֹסִיף לָנוּ לַעֲבוֹדָתֶךָ. וּבְצֵל כְּנָפֶיךָ תַּסְתִּירֵנוּ. וְתַצִּילֵנוּ לָנוּ וּלְכָל בְּנֵי בֵיתֵנוּ מִכָּל גְּזֵרוֹת קָשׁוֹת וְרָעוֹת, וְנִהְיֶה שְׁקֵטִים וְשַׁאֲנַנִּים, דְּשֵׁנִים וְרַעֲנַנִּים לַעֲבוֹדָתֶךָ וּלְיִרְאָתֶךָ.

PRAYER FOR HEALTH
(Composed by the Chida)

Hashem, with your compassion, grant us strength and health, and full faculties; give strength and might to our limbs and organs, our ligaments and sinews, and our entire bodies, so that our good health may be guarded, and that no ache or pain shall befall us. Let us be happy and good and healthy, so that we can serve you. Protect us from all evil; prolong our days with goodness and our years with pleasantness, and let us live to fill our allotment of years. Length of days and years of life, increase for us — so that we may serve You. In the shade of Your sheltering wings, may You conceal us and save us and all of our family members from harsh and cruel decrees. Let us be tranquil and serene, enriched and invigorated to serve You in awe.

GLOSSARY

bais medrash — House of Study

bentsch — recitation of the Grace After Meals

besuros tovos — good news

b'ezras Hashem — with God's help

binah — understanding

bitachon — trust in God

bracha/brachos — blessing/blessings

chachmah — wisdom

chizuk — encouragement and inspiration

chuppah — wedding canopy

daas — knowledge

daven — pray

din — judgment

emunah — faith

frum — religious

galus — exile

gemara — Talmud

HaKadosh Baruch Hu — God (literally The Holy One, Blessed is He)

halachah — Jewish law

hashgacha — Divine Providence

hatzlacha — success

havdalah — ceremony marking the end of the Sabbath

heter — dispensation

hishtadlus — effort

Imahos — Matriarchs

kashrus — kosher status

kavanah – devotion (spiritual intention)

kedusha — holiness

Kiddush — blessing over the wine sanctifying the Sabbath and holidays

kiruv — outreach

Klal Yisroel — the Jewish nation

lashon hora — gossip

Maariv — Evening Prayer

GLOSSARY

mahn — manna

malachim — angels

mazal — fortune

Meforshim — commentaries

melava malka — special meal after the Sabbath

Mesilas Yeshorim — Path of the Just (ethical work written by Rabbi Moshe Chaim Luzzatto)

Mishnah — Oral Law

mitzvah — commandment

mitzvah of challah — mitzvah to separate a small portion of the challah dough, to burn it and discard it. During the time of the Temple this separated piece was dedicated to the Kohen.

Modeh Ani — prayer said upon rising in the morning

Mussaf — additional prayer said on Sabbath and holidays

Mussar — ethical teachings

nachas — pride and joy

neshamah — soul

Nine Days — The last nine days of the "Three Weeks" period (see below), a time of increased mourning culminating on Tisha B'av (see below).

nisayon/nisyonos — challenge/challenges

pareve — neutral, neither dairy nor meat

pasuk — verse

Pesach — Passover

Ribono Shel Olam — Master of the world

sefer — Jewish text

Sefirah —The literal meaning refers to a "count" of the 49 days between Pesach (Passover) and Shavuos (Festival of Weeks). It is also a period of semimourning in commemoration of the great students of Rabbi Akiva who perished in a plague during this period.

segulah — fortuitous

seudos — meals

shadchan — matchmaker

shalom bayis — domestic harmony

Shalosh Seudos — third meal of the Sabbath

Shamayim — the Heavens

shemittah — Sabbatical year [for the land in Israel]

Shemone Esrei — silent prayer of eighteen blessings

shidduchim — matrimonial matches

shiur — lecture

shul — synagogue

GLOSSARY

Shulchan Aruch — Code of Jewish Law

simcha/b'simcha — happiness/happy

siyata d'shmaya — Divine Assistance

Taanis Bechorim — fast for the eldest male in the family on the eve of Passover

tallis — prayer shawl

tefillah — prayer

teshuvah — repentance

Three Weeks — The period between the 17th day of the Hebrew month of Tammuz and the 9th day of the Hebrew month of Av when we mourn the destruction of the Temple.

Tisha B'Av — Lit., the ninth day of Av, the saddest day on the Jewish calendar, marking the date when both Temples were set afire and destroyed.

treif — non-kosher

tzaar — pain

tzaddik — righteous person

yagon — distress

Yom Tov — holiday

zemiros — traditional hymns of the Sabbath and holidays

z"l or ztl. — Hebrew abbreviation meaning "may his memory be a blessing"

THE FIVE BOOKS OF MOSES

Bereishis	Genesis
Shemos	Exodus
Vayikra	Leviticus
Bamidbar	Numbers
Devarim	Deuteronomy

PROPHETS AND WRITINGS

Koheles	Ecclesiastes
Mishlei	Proverbs
Shmuel II	Samuel II
Tehillim	Psalms
Yeshayah	Isaiah

Biographical Sketches

Brisker Rav — Rabbi Yitzchok Zev Soloveichik (1886 –1959)

Chazon Ish — Rabbi Avrohom Yeshayah Karelitz (1878-1953)

Chofetz Chaim — Rabbi Yisroel Meir Kagan (1838-1933)

Eitz Yosef — Rabbi Chanoch Zundel ben Yosef of Bialystok, Poland, early 19th century

Kotzker Rebbe — Rabbi Menachem Mendel Morgenstern of Kotzk (1787-1859)

Mabit — Rabbi Moshe Ben Yosef di Trani (1505-1585)

Malbim — Rabbi Meir Leib Ben Yechiel Michael (1808-1879)

Rabbi Avrohom Yaakov Pam — Rosh Yeshiva of Yeshiva Torah Vodaas (1913-2001)

Rabbi Elazar Menachem Man Shach — preeminent leader of Torah Jewry (1898-2001)

Rabbi Elchonon Wasserman — one of the Chofetz Chaim's closest disciples and world renowned Torah sage (1874-1941)

Rabbi Nachman of Breslov — founder of the Breslov Chassidic dynasty and great Chassidic master (1772-1810)

Rabbi Shlomo Wolbe – contemporary Torah sage (1914-2005)

Rabbi Yaakov Leiner of Ishbitz — son of Rabbi Mordechai Yosef and successor to the Ishbitza-Radzyn dynasty (19th century)

Rambam / Hilchos Dei'os — Maimonides, Rabbi Moses ben Maimon (1135-1204) / Laws of Knowledge

Reb Chaim of Sanz — Rabbi Chaim Halberstam of Sanz, Poland (1793-1876)

Reb Noach of Lechovich — Rabbi Noach Perlow (1773-1832)

Reb Simcha Bunim of Psischa — great Chassidic master (1765-1827)

Tzemach Dovid — Rabbi David Ganz (late 16th century)

Vilna Gaon — Rabbi Eliyahu ben Shlomo Zalman (1720-1797)

About the Author

Rabbi Dovid Goldwasser, of Brooklyn's Congregation Bais Yitzchok, is known for his exceptional ability to captivate and inspire audiences worldwide. This highly regarded rabbi is a renowned speaker, syndicated columnist, university professor and has authored many books. His popular radio commentary on New Jersey's WFMU and New York's WSNR. attracts large audiences daily.

Rabbi Goldwasser provides reassurance and inspiration, counseling young people, couples and families globally. For the last twenty years he has been a leading proponent in the Jewish community for the prompt recognition of eating disorders and its proper treatment. He works closely with medical personnel and mental health professionals, facilities, and their patients and has written extensively on the subject of eating disorders.

Rabbi Goldwasser proudly participated in the development of a suitable curriculum geared to the sensitivities of observant community to promote healthy body image, eating fitness and the weight in children that was implemented in schools throughout the U.S. on the elementary level.

Recently, Rabbi Goldwasser has delivered a paper at the Nefesh International Conference for Mental Health in New York focusing on the spiritual conflicts experienced by eating disordered patients. He also presented at Renfrew Center Foundation for Eating Disorders on "The Societal Factors in Eating Disorders", and lectured at the Princeton University Medical Center, in regard to understanding the religious, moral and ethical character of the observant Jew. At the National Convention of Agudath Israel of America Rabbi Goldwasser presented a paper on "At-Risk Behaviors: Problems and Solutions." Rabbi Goldwasser has addressed the topic of "Promoting Self-Esteem and Positive Body Image" at a conference of the Orthodox Union held at Sheppard Pratt in Baltimore, MD. At Long Island Jewish Hospital, Rabbi Goldwasser addressed the topic of counseling the observant eating disordered patient. In London, England, he presented at a conference of mental health professionals on the subject of eating disorders and alternative modalities in treatment. Rabbi Goldwasser has been recognized for his work by both Maimonides Medical Center of Brooklyn, NY and HEED of New York University Medical Center.